SUPERVISORY MANAGEMENT

FOR HOSPITALS AND RELATED HEALTH FACILITIES

SUPERVISORY MANAGEMENT

FOR HOSPITALS AND RELATED HEALTH FACILITIES

THEO HAIMANN, Ph.D.
Professor of Business Administration
St. Louis University
St. Louis, Missouri

THE CATHOLIC HOSPITAL ASSOCIATION
St. Louis, Missouri 63104

To
Ruthie
Lyn and Mark

PREFACE

This book is intended for supervisory personnel engaged in the work of hospitals and related health facilities such as nursing homes, homes for the aged, rehabilitation centers, long-term care facilities, and other institutions of this type. Supervisors are becoming increasingly aware of the need to develop new perspectives, to gain new insights into human relationships, and to stay on top of their jobs, in brief, to be better managers. This text is intended to be an aid in this direction. Its purpose is to demonstrate to the supervisor that proficiency in management will better equip him to cope with the ever-increasing demands of getting the job done, contribute more effectively to the overall goals of his institution, at the same time making him more valuable to the administrator.

The text is written for supervisors, not for administrators, although most of its content would be of great interest to the latter also. The common denominator of all supervisors is the part they play as managers within the administrative hierarchy of the institution. Because of the ever-increasing demands of the technical specialties, this role has often been overlooked. Without going into the technical aspects of specific supervisory positions, the book discusses the managerial aspects common to all supervisory jobs whether they are in nursing, medical records, medical social work, housekeeping, dietary, laboratory, laundry, maintenance, engineering, or any of the numerous other specialties.

The supervisory position is the most critical point in any organization, namely, the supervision of people in the day-to-day running of an institution. In industrial and commercial enterprises it is generally recognized that the supervisory job is a most demanding and exacting one. A wealth of excellent material in the field of supervision is available for business and industry. This book has been written for the purpose of applying such material from industry and business to the area of hospitals and related fields. It is an established fact that hospitals and related enterprises comprise one of the largest industries in the United States. Provision for health care will become more complex due to its rapidly expanding activities, government support, increase in population, and advances of scientific medicine. In addition to this, it is imperative that all health care facilities keep pace with the social and scientific progress of civilization. This means an ever-increasing challenge for efficient administration capable of coping with more complex problems, whether they are of an economic, professional, scientific or educational nature. This creates an increasing need for capable, well-trained administrators, and in turn a need for supervisors who are able to run their departments efficiently.

In hospitals and all other related health facilities, the supervisor's position is exceptionally strategic since in most cases the recipient does not elect to receive the services provided, nor does he understand them. The supervisor in a hospital and other related health facilities also must contend with emotional factors involved in the care of the patients and their relatives under conditions which make effective supervision unusually difficult. In addition to this, the supervisor is often torn between considerations of a professional nature and those of an administrative nature. All of these factors make it imperative for the supervisor to be a capable manager of his department.

The book is concerned with the managerial process, examining the managerial functions of planning, organizing, staffing, directing, and controlling and their relation to the daily job of the supervisor. In reality, all of these functions are closely related and such a distinct classification is scarcely discernible. But such a presentation makes possible a methodological, clear and complete analysis of the managerial functions of a supervisor. Since it is the supervisor's job to get things done with and through the help of people, it follows that he must of necessity be concerned with the human aspects of supervision. The art of getting things done with and through people has its foundation in this relationship between the supervisor and the people with whom he works. Nevertheless, it is essential that in bringing behavorial factors into play, the supervisor should be thoroughly familiar with the conceptual framework of managing. This book obviously is not an all-comprising text on supervision. It would be presumptuous to assume that this one short volume could cover all possible supervisory problems. Emphasis in this text is on balance. Human relations are kept in proper perspective with relation to the other aspects of the supervisory job.

This book is introductory in the sense that it assumes no previous knowledge on the part of the reader. But it also includes material of a sophisticated nature which can be understood without undue difficulties. It will help the newly appointed supervisor become acquainted with the many problems which will face him, and it offers practical advice for their solution. For the experienced supervisors it is intended to refresh thinking and widen horizons by taking a different and challenging look at both their own position and that of their employees.

Material for this text has come from writings and research of scholars in the area of management and the social sciences, and from the experience of numerous supervisors, managers and administrators. In addition to the author's own experience in practice, this text also reflects his experiences in teaching management, from the stimulating discussions emanating from supervisory development programs, lectures to administrators and supervisors at different levels in the administrative hierarchy of hospitals and related health facilities, and from his consulting activities.

In writing a book such as this, the author is indebted to so many persons that it is impossible to give them all due credit. Special thanks go to my wife, Ruth, for her patient and skillful editorial assistance. The author also wishes to acknowledge with thanks the help and encouragement given by the Catholic Hospital Association of the United States and Canada, and especially to Father John J. Flanagan, S.J., its Director, and to Mr. Charles Berry, the Associate Director. Last but by no means least, thanks go to Mrs. Selma Schlafman who skillfully transcribed many challenging notes into readable manuscript. To all these the author extends grateful thanks while bearing responsibility for any sins of omission or commission.

Theo Haimann.

Saint Louis, Missouri
June, 1965

CONTENTS

PART VI   CONTROLLING

PART VII   LABOR RELATIONS

PART I

BASIC
CONSIDERATIONS

1

INTRODUCTION

The task of a supervisor or a department head in a hospital or in any other related health facility is a demanding one. You probably have learned this from your own experience, or by observing supervisors in hospitals and related institutions as they go about their daily jobs. The supervisor is the link between the employee and the administration. To his employees, the supervisor represents the administration of the institution, and the supervisor is the only contact they ever have with members of the management group. The supervisor is the person in the middle who has to carry water on both shoulders. He is that part of management who must make certain that the job gets done. To his employees he must be a good leader. But not only must the supervisor be a good boss with technical competence and other qualities, he must also be a competent subordinate to the manager above him—in most instances, the administrator or an associate administrator. In this respect he must be a good follower. Furthermore, the supervisor must maintain satisfactory relationships with the heads of all other departments and services. The relationship to them must be that of a colleague who is willing to cooperate and eager to coordinate his department's efforts to reach the enterprise's objectives and goals.

It is commonly acknowledged in industrial and commercial

1

undertakings that the role of the first line supervisor is a most difficult one. It is even more difficult for supervisors within a hospital and related health care facilities, because their activities eventually influence the welfare of the patients and the smooth functioning of the hospital. In addition to their many obligations, the supervisors must always bear in mind the desires and needs of patients and their relatives, who at the time are physically and emotionally upset people. The supervisor should be continuously aware of the problems of human relations among medical staff members as well as between all the other hospital personnel and patients, in order to accomplish the objective: the restoration of the patients' health. All of this makes the job of the supervisor a difficult one.

Let us look at the work which is required of the supervisor of the housekeeping department. Generally, a job description will tell you that it is the supervisor's job to maintain the hospital in clean and orderly condition. She should be able to teach both prevailing and new methods, and demonstrate these with equipment. She must continuously study new cleaning methods and new cleaning equipment, and recommend changes of layout and location of equipment, if necessary, to facilitate the cleaning of various areas of the hospital. She plans and directs the work schedule for the staff, taking into consideration visiting hours, traffic, and the work to be completed. She is expected to write instruction sheets and training manuals for housekeeping procedures. She must periodically inspect the completed work for the quality of service. In addition to this, she will plan and select furnishings for the various rooms, considering serviceability, decorative appeal, and other factors.

In addition, the housekeeping supervisor must develop and maintain effective working relationships with the professional, administrative, and maintenance personnel of the institution. Furthermore, she is expected to interview and make the final selection of applicants who have been referred to her by the personnel department. She is the one whose job it is to dismiss unsatisfactory employees and to take disciplinary action whenever necessary. In addition to all of this, there are many other duties connected with the job of the supervisor of the housekeeping department. This by itself is a very impressive arrangement of duties and obligations, making this a good-size job. But with our growing, complex society the job of a hospital supervisor will become even more challenging.

In reality, the job of any supervisor consists of two main components. First of all, he must have a thorough knowledge of the job to be performed and be technically competent to do the job in question. The other aspect of the supervisor's job is that he must also be a manager. It is this managerial aspect of the supervisory job which will significantly determine the effectiveness of his performance.

You may have observed various supervisors at different occasions and noticed that some of them are usually harassed, continuously involved in doing the job at hand; they are muddling through and are knee-deep in work. These supervisors put in hard and long hours, are utterly devoted to the job, never afraid of doing anything themselves, and so on. They are supervisors who are working exceedingly hard. But they never seem to have enough time left to actually supervise. And then again, you may have observed supervisors who seem to be on top of the job, and have their departments functioning smoothly and orderly. They have found the time to sit at their desks at least part of the day and have been able to keep their desk work up to date. Why is there a difference? you may ask. Of course, there are some supervisors who are basically more capable than others. If you compare two chief engineers in two hospitals whose equipment is almost alike, and if you try to find out why one chief engineer is on top of the job and the other is continuously fixing things himself, you may find the reason in the fact that the one understands his job better than the other. Undoubtedly, there are better and poorer mechanics. But let us assume that both are equally good mechanics and still we will find that there are those whose job gets them down and that others are on top of the job. They both have similar equipment under their care and the conditions under which they perform are about alike. Still, the results of the one are significantly better than those of the other. Why is this? The answer is that the one is a better manager, that he is in a position to manage the functions of his department in a managerial, administrative manner, and in so doing gets the job done with and through the people of his department. The difference

3

between a good supervisor and a poor supervisor, assuming that their technical skill is alike, is the difference in their managerial ability. It is this aspect of the supervisory job which we intend to study.

The managerial aspect of the supervisor's position has been neglected for too long. Most stress has always been put on the technical competence of doing the job within a particular department. Consider your own job. It is very likely that you were appointed to this job from the ranks of one of the various professional services or crafts, and, due to your particular ingenuity, effort, and willingness to work hard, you were put into this supervisory position. When you were appointed as supervisor you were put into this position in order to assume some of the responsibilities of management. But precious little was done to acquaint you with these responsibilities and, what is even more important, very little was done to help you to cope with the managerial aspects of your new job, once you had assumed it. More or less overnight you were made a part of management without having been prepared to be a manager. Ever since, you have done the best you could and your department is functioning reasonably well. But you do have your problems, and the time has come for you to stress the managerial aspects of your job so that you will be the manager, that you will be running the department instead of the department running you. The aim of this text is to show the supervisor how to become a better manager. This does not mean that he can neglect getting the job done so far as the technical aspects are concerned. Never underestimate that part of the job. As you know, one of the requirements of a good supervisor is that he thoroughly understand the technical operation. Often the supervisor actually is the most skilled workman of the department, and he can do a more efficient and quicker job. But the supervisor must not be tempted to step in and take the job over, unless for the purpose of instruction or in an emergency. Your responsibility as a supervisor is to see to it that your employees can do the job, and do it properly. As a manager you plan, guide, and supervise. Therefore, let us concentrate on the managerial aspects.

First, let us consider what is meant by management. Stated simply, management is the function of getting things done through people and with people, and directing the efforts of individuals toward a common objective. You have long learned from your own experience that in most endeavors one person can accomplish relatively little by himself. For this reason, most people have found it expedient and even necessary to join with others in order to attain the goals of an enterprise. It is the manager's function to achieve this goal, with the help of his subordinates and employees. Those who hold managerial positions significantly influence the effectiveness with which people work together and attain their stated objectives and goals. Your managerial function as supervisor of your department is to get the job of your division done through and with the help of your employees. The better manager you are the better the results of your department will be.

It may come as a surprise to you to learn that the managerial aspects of all supervisory jobs are the same, regardless of the function in which you are engaged. The managerial content of your supervisory position is the same whether you are the head of the housekeeping division, the chief engineer in your maintenance department, the supervisor of nursing, the food service supervisor, or the supervisor of any of the other departments or services. And, by the same token, the managerial functions are the same regardless of the level within the administrative hierarchy on which you find yourself. It does not matter whether you are the supervisor on the firing line, whether you are in middle level management, or within the top administrative group. The functions of the manager are the same. And in addition to this, it does not matter in which kind of organization you are working. The managerial functions are the same whether the supervisor is working in an industrial enterprise, commercial enterprise, non-profit organization, fraternal organization, government, or in a hospital and other related health facility. The manager's job is the same. He performs the same functions in all of these organizations regardless of his specialty and regardless of the rung on which he finds himself on the administrative ladder.

These managerial skills, however, must be distinguished from technical skills. As stated above, all supervisors must possess special technical skills and know-how in the particular field which they supervise in their daily work. But in addition to being an

5

expert in these technical areas, a supervisor must also possess managerial skills. In his supervisory position he is requested to employ both. But as you advance upward in the managerial ladder, you will find that you will practice fewer technical skills, and it will become increasingly important for you to apply the managerial skills rather than your technical ones. If you will observe throughout your own institution, you will find that the higher you go within the administrative hierarchy, the more administrative skills are required and the less technical know-how. Therefore, the top administrator usually possesses far fewer technical skills than those who are employed under him. But in his growth to the top the administrator has acquired all the necessary administrative skills for the management of the entire enterprise.

But our statement above, that all managers perform the same functions regardless of their administrative rank, still holds true. The only difference is that the higher up you are in the managerial hierarchy, the more emphasis you will put on the managing aspect rather than the technical specialties. Therefore, the hospital administrator should be concerned primarily with the management of the overall activities of the hospital and his functions are purely administrative. In this endeavor, of course, he depends on the help of his various subordinate administrators and managers, including all the supervisors, to get the job done. The administrator, in turn, uses his managerial skills in directing the efforts of all subordinate managers toward the common objectives for the good of the hospital. Therefore, throughout the organization the purpose of the managerial functions is the same, regardless of the level within the administrative hierarchy.

In this text we shall use the terms 'supervisor' or 'manager' interchangeably. We shall refer to supervisory, managerial, and administrative functions as the same. There are some fine distinctions between these terms, but for our purposes we can ignore this and all of these terms will mean the same thing.

MANAGERIAL SKILLS CAN BE LEARNED   It is generally recognized beyond any doubt that the managerial skills can be learned. They are not something with which you are necessarily born or not born. It is often stated that good managers, like good athletes, are born, not made. This belief is about as incorrect in the one case as it is in the other. It cannot be denied that men are born with different physiological and biological potential, and that they are endowed with an unequal amount of intelligence and many other characteristics and potentialities. It is true that a man who is not a natural athlete is not likely to run one hundred yards in record time. But many men who are natural athletes have not come close to that goal either.

A good athlete is made when a man with some natural endowment, by practice, learning, efforts, sacrifice, and experience develops the natural endowment into a mature skill. The same holds true for a good manager; by practice, learning, and experience he develops his natural endowment of intelligence and characteristics into a mature skill of a good manager. The skills involved in managing are as learnable and trainable as the skills in playing tennis. The position which you hold now and those which you have held before should convince you that you do have the necessary prerequisites in order to progress and acquire the skills of a manager.

The benefits which you as a supervisor will derive from learning to be a better manager are obvious. First of all, you have much opportunity to apply the managerial principles and your managerial knowledge in the very job in which you are now as a supervisor. Good management as a supervisor will make all the difference in the world in the performance of your department. You will find that applying the principles of management to your work will make for a smoother functioning department where the work gets done on time, where your workers willingly and enthusiastically contribute toward the ultimate objective. You will find that you will stay within the expenditures allowed to you. The application of good management principles will put you, as a supervisor, on top of your job, instead of being completely swallowed up by it. You will find that you will have more time to be concerned with the overall aspects of your department and in so doing you will become more valuable to those to whom you are responsible. You are more likely to contribute significantly with suggestions and advice to the administrator in many areas in which you have never been consulted before but questions which ultimately affect your department.

7

You will see the overall aspects of the various departments and their interrelationships. And good management will enable you to work in closer harmony with your colleagues who are supervising other departments. Briefly, you will do a more effective job with much less effort.

Managerial skills, of course, will not be learned overnight. You can only become a manager by managing; that means by applying the principles of management to your work situation. As you go on, you will no doubt make mistakes here and there but, in turn, you will learn from your mistakes. These principles of management which we shall discuss in this course will be definite guidelines you can apply in most situations. They will help you to avoid errors which often take a long time to correct. Your efforts to become an outstanding supervisor will pay you handsome dividends. As your managerial competence increases, you will be able to prevent many of the difficulties which make a job a burden to many supervisors instead of a challenging and satisfying task.

In addition to the direct benefits of doing a better supervisory job, there are other benefits. You, personally, as a supervisor, will grow in stature, and as time goes on you will be capable of handling larger and more complicated assignments. Briefly, it will enable you to fill better and higher paying jobs. You will move up within the managerial hierarchy and it is only natural that as a good supervisor you will want to improve yourself at the same time. An additional satisfying thought is that the principles of management are equally applicable in any organization and in all managerial and supervisory positions.

As stated above, the principles of management required to produce gyroscopes, to manage a retail department, to supervise the office work, to run a garage, are all the same. The principles of management, by and large, are applicable not only here in this country, but all over the world. Aside from local peculiarities and questions of personalities, it would not matter whether you are the supervisor of a department in a textile mill in India, the supervisor in a chemical plant in Italy, the supervisor of mechanics in France, the foreman of a department in a steel mill in Gary, Indiana, or the supervisor of the food service section in a hospital and any other related health facility. By becoming a manager you will become less dependent on the specialty in which you have grown up. You become more moveable in every direction and in every respect.

Obviously, these are great inducements for you to become acquainted with the principles of good management which you first can put to use in your present activities. Later on they will help you to go on from there to better and more responsible positions.

2

THE EARMARKS OF A MANAGER

There are two criteria which will quickly indicate whether or not a member of your organization is a manager. These earmarks are simply the answers to the following two questions: One, does he perform the managerial functions, and two, does he have authority? If both of these questions can be answered in the positive, then you are speaking about a manager in the true sense of the word. But if either one of the two components is lacking, regardless of the best intentions, and regardless of all the outward trappings, you are not confronted with a manager. Let us therefore examine both of these chief components of the manager's position.

THE MANAGERIAL FUNCTIONS

First we shall discuss the managerial functions. The five managerial functions a manager performs are planning, organizing, staffing, directing, and controlling. The terminology which is used to describe the managerial functions varies from time to time. Also, some consider the managerial functions to be only four instead of five, and others cite six instead of five. But by and large, we will do well to use the five as outlined above and this shall be the framework of our discussion throughout this text. What does it mean when we say the managerial functions are planning, organizing, staffing, directing, and controlling?

PLANNING   Planning is a function that determines in advance what should be done. It consists of determining the goals, the objectives, policies, procedures, methods, and all other means of achieving these objectives of your undertaking. In planning, the manager must think of the various alternative plans which are available to him. Planning is mental work; it is intellectual

10

in nature. It is looking ahead and preparing for the future. It is laying out in advance the road to be followed, the way the job has to be done. Often you have observed supervisors who are fighting one crisis after another. The probable reason for this is that they did not plan. They did not look ahead. It is every manager's duty to plan and this cannot be delegated to someone else. Yes, you may call on the help of certain specialists to give you some assistance in laying out the various plans; but by and large it is up to you, as the manager of the department, to make your own plans. Of course, these plans must coincide with the general overall objectives as laid down by the administrator of the hospital. Aside from these general overall directives and general boundaries, it is up to you to lay out the path, the plans for your own department. Planning must come before you can perform any of the other managerial functions. But even as the manager proceeds with his other managerial functions he continues to plan, revising his plans and choosing different alternatives as the need arises. Therefore, although planning is a primary function, the supervisor continues to plan all the time as he performs his other managerial functions. More will be said about this later on.

ORGANIZING　To organize means to give the answer to the question of how the work in the section will be divided and accomplished. To answer this the manager has to define, group, and assign job duties. When the supervisor organizes he determines and enumerates the various activities which are required, he assigns these activities, and at the same time he delegates the necessary authority to provide for the various functions. He divides and groups the work into individual jobs and defines the relationship between them. To organize means to design a structural framework within which the various duties of the supervisors' departments are to be performed and how they should be performed. Of course, this structural framework of your department must fit into the overall structure of the institution. When the manager organizes this structural framework, he will also see to it that the authority relationships between the various department managers are appropriately aligned. While organizing he will of necessity have to delegate some authority

11

which, as we shall see in a little while, is absolutely essential for a manager to possess in order to effectively manage. It is in this organizing function that the manager clarifies problems of authority and responsibility within his department. This will be considered more fully later on.

STAFFING   By staffing, we understand the supervisor's responsibility to recruit new employees and to make certain that there are enough qualified employees available to fill the various positions needed in the department. Staffing involves the selection and training of these employees. It involves the problem of promoting them, of appraising their performance from time to time, of giving them further opportunities for development. In addition to this, staffing includes a wise and appropriate system and rate of pay.

DIRECTING   The directing function of a manager includes guiding, teaching, coaching, and supervising his subordinates. To direct means to issue directives so that the various jobs get done. It is the manager's job to develop the abilities of his workers by directing, teaching, and coaching them effectively. As you know, the job must get done, and without orders and directives very little is likely to be accomplished. The managerial function of directing means the issuing of orders and directives, and in addition to this, the guidance and overseeing of the subordinates. It is not sufficient for a manager to plan, organize, and have enough employees available. The manager must stimulate action by giving orders to his subordinates and by supervising them as they go about their work. Directing is a process around which all performance revolves; it is the essence of all operations. As you know from your own experience, much of your time is spent in directing your subordinates—as a matter of fact, probably most of your time is spent in this way.

CONTROLLING   The managerial function of control involves those activities that are necessary in seeing to it that objectives are achieved as planned. To control means to determine whether or not the plans are being met, whether or not progress is being made toward the objective, and to act, if necessary, to correct any deviations and shortcomings. Here again we can see the importance of planning as a primary function of the manager. It would not be possible for him to check whether or not the work was proceeding properly if there were no plans against which to check. To control does not mean only to make sure that the objectives are achieved. But to control also includes taking corrective action, in the event that there is a failure to achieve these objectives.

It is helpful to think of these five managerial functions as a circular continuous movement. As a matter of fact, in your daily supervisory activities you have often felt that your job looks like a vicious circle without a beginning and without an end. However, if you look at the managerial process as a circle consisting of these five different functions, it will greatly simplify your job of managing. These five functions flow into each other, as may be seen in Figure 1, and at times there is no clear line of demarcation where the one ends and the other function begins. Also, it is not possible for any manager to set aside a certain amount of time for one or another function, as the effort spent in one function will vary as the conditions and circumstances

FIGURE 1

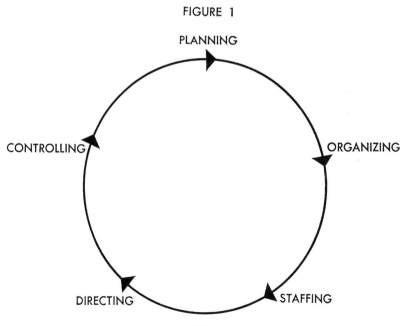

PLANNING

CONTROLLING

ORGANIZING

DIRECTING

STAFFING

change. But there is little doubt that planning must come first. Without plans the manager cannot organize, staff, direct, or control. Therefore, in our discussions we shall follow this sequence of planning, organizing, staffing, directing, and controlling.

As stated above, these five managerial functions are universal. They are the managerial functions of all managers whether they be the chairman of the board, the administrator, or the supervisor on the firing line. All of them perform all five functions. However, the time and effort which each manager will devote to each of these five functions will vary, depending on the level within the administrative hierarchy on which he finds himself. It is likely that the administrator will spend more time in the planning and organizing function and less time staffing, directing, and controlling. However, the supervisor of a department will probably spend less time planning and organizing and more of his time will be spent in staffing, and particularly in directing and controlling. But they all perform the same managerial functions. The administrator will plan, let us say, for six months ahead, one year ahead, or even for five years ahead. You, as a supervisor, will make plans of much shorter duration. There are times when you will have plans for six months or so, but very frequently you may just make your plans for the next four weeks, this week, or even for this day. In other words, the span and the magnitude of your plans will be smaller. Nevertheless, you, as a supervisor, will plan just as the administrator plans. The only difference is the magnitude of the plans. The same is true, for example, for the directing function. The administrator, if he is a capable administrator, will spend a minimum of time in directing and supervising. You, as a supervisor, however, are concerned with getting the job done each and every day, and you will have to spend a large part of your efforts in this directing function. Therefore, what we stated above is correct: all managers perform the same managerial functions regardless of the level in the hierarchy. The time and effort involved in each of these functions will depend on the rung of the administrative ladder on which you find yourself. This is illustrated in Figure 2. And by the same token let us not forget that unless you perform all of these five functions, you are not fulfilling your managerial duties.

FIGURE 2

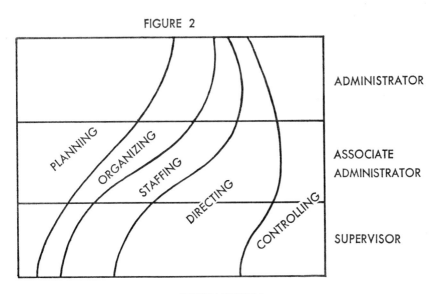

ADMINISTRATOR

ASSOCIATE
ADMINISTRATOR

SUPERVISOR

AUTHORITY

The second factor which earmarks a manager as such is the possession of authority. Authority is the key to the managerial job. Without it you are not a manager. In one of the following chapters (Chapter 5) we shall discuss at great length the meaning of authority and its counterpart, responsibility. However, it is necessary to introduce this concept briefly at this time, as it is one of the two essential characteristics of the managerial position.

What, then, is this authority without which the supervisor is not a manager? What is authority which makes the managerial position real? Briefly speaking, and without going into the details of the concept of authority, let it be sufficient to say at this time that in a framework of business management, authority is defined as legal or rightful power, the right to command and to act. It is the power by which a manager can ask his subordinates to do or not to do a certain thing which the manager, the man who possesses the authority, deems appropriate and necessary in order to realize the objectives of the department. This concept of authority includes the possession of the power to impose sanctions and to coerce, because without such power to enforce an order the enterprise could become disorganized and chaos would result. In case the worker refuses to carry out the directive, the manager's authority includes his power and right to take disciplinary action and, in the last instance, to discharge the subordinate. Of course, this power has restrictions in many respects. We shall discuss this in the chapter on authority and responsibility (Chapter 5).

Every successful manager knows that in order to induce his workers to perform required duties it is best not to fall back on authority but to utilize other ways and means for getting the job done. We all know that it is far better not to depend on this concept of power and authority; as a matter of fact, in practice it has come to the point where most managers do not even speak of authority at any time. They prefer to speak of "responsibility" or "tasks" or "duties" which they have, instead of stating that they possess authority. Some managers rightfully consider it better human relations to say that they have the responsibility for certain activities instead of saying that they have the authority within that area. Using the words responsibility, tasks and duties in a loose sense allows the manager to avoid the big stick.

But you as the supervisor should not be misled by using these terms in their improper sense. Properly used, you as a supervisor should know that having authority delegated to you means that you have the power and right to issue orders. You must know that, properly stated, tasks and duties have been assigned to you. You also must know that you have accepted the responsibility and this responsibility has been exacted from you by your superior. All of this will be discussed in detail later on.

As stated above, for the time being we shall define authority as the rightful legal power to request a subordinate to do a certain thing or to refrain from doing so. If he does not follow these instructions the manager is in a position to take disciplinary action, even to discharge the subordinate. There are much better ways of exercising one's authority than to dismiss the worker and there are better human relations practices which will bring about the desired results. There also are many other restrictions which will influence the supervisor not to invoke such drastic action. These restrictions may be in the nature of legal restrictions, union contracts, or other considerations of morals, ethics, and human behavior.

However, we want to avoid the danger of confusing the issue as to what authority really is, where it lies in the organization, and how it manifests itself. Regardless of how the manager applies authority, the point to remember is that a manager must have it. Without it he is no manager; his job is not real. Without the right to give orders to workers there would be no superior and no subordinate. Without authority only anarchy and chaos would result.

As stated above, we will discuss at length in Chapter 5 what the various considerations for authority are, how you as a supervisor will have to look at it, and how it will make your managerial position a reality. At that time we will also discuss the concept of responsibility, which is always connected with authority. They go with each other; the one does not exist without the other. At that time we shall also examine how your subordinates and workers react to authority. At that occasion we shall also discuss delegation of authority. This latter means the process which enables you to receive this authority from your superior manager, and the process which you will use in order to delegate some of the authority which has been delegated to you onto your subordinate managers. Just as the possession of authority is the lifeblood of the managerial position, this process of delegating authority to the lower ranks within the managerial hierarchy makes it possible to build an organization structure with effective managers on each level. A more detailed dicussion of authority and responsibility and the process of delegation will follow. It is introduced at this point only to clarify one of the basic earmarks of the managerial job, and the explanations given up to now will suffice for us to build further.

COORDINATION

We defined management as a process of getting things done through and with the help of your employees. We defined it as directing the efforts of individuals toward a common objective. In the final analysis, this means that management is the coordination of the efforts of the various members of an organization. As a matter of fact, some writers have even defined management as the task of achieving coordination. You can look at coordination as the orderly synchronization of efforts of your workers to provide the proper amount, timing, and quality of execution so that their unified efforts lead to the stated objective, namely, the common purpose of the enterprise. Some writers have preferred to look at coordination as a separate managerial function. But we prefer to look at coordination not as a separate function of the manager, but as a process by which the manager achieves orderly group effort and unity of action in the pursuit of the common purpose. The manager brings about this process while he performs the five basic managerial functions of planning, organizing, staffing, directing, and controlling. The resulting coordination, the resulting synchronization of efforts, should be one of the goals the manager keeps in mind when he performs his five managerial functions.

At this point you can see that the path of achieving coordination is a much more difficult one on the administrator's level than on your supervisory level. The administrator has to achieve the synchronization of effort throughout the entire organization, throughout very many departments. You as a supervisor of only one department have this task to achieve coordination only within your own division. But, nevertheless, the achievement of coordination is necessary, regardless of the scope of your division. You will do well to look at coordination as something which comes about as you are performing your five managerial functions appropriately. Coordination should result as a by-product of the performance of the managerial functions, and it should not be looked upon as a separate managerial function. You as a supervisor will bear coordination in mind in everything you do when performing your managerial functions. The synchronization of the efforts of your subordinates should be uppermost in your thoughts whenever you plan, organize, staff, direct, and control.

COORDINATION AND COOPERATION   The term coordination must not be confused with cooperation, for there is considerable difference between them. Cooperation indicates merely the willingness of individuals to help each other. It is the result of a voluntary attitude of a group of people. Coordination is much more inclusive, requiring more than the mere desire and willingness of the participants. For instance, consider a group

18

of men attempting to move a heavy object. They are sufficient in number, willing and eager to cooperate with each other and trying to do their best to move the object. They are also fully aware of their common purpose. However, in all likelihood their efforts will be of little avail until one of them—the manager—gives the proper orders to apply the right amount of effort at the right place at the right time, and then they can move the object. It is possible that by sheer coincidence mere cooperation could have brought about the desired result in an instance such as the above. But no manager can afford to rely upon such a coincidental occurrence. Although cooperation is always helpful and the lack of it could prevent all possibility of coordination, its mere presence will not assure coordination. Coordination is superior in order of importance to cooperation.

ATTAINING COORDINATION Coordination is not easily attained, and the task of coordination is becoming increasingly complex the more difficult the various duties become. With the growth of an organization the task of synchronizing the daily activities becomes more and more complicated. As the number of positions in your department increases, the need for coordination and the necessity for synchronization to secure the unified result increases. Specialization is another source from which problems of coordination stem. And human nature in itself presents problems of coordination, since each and every one of your employees is preoccupied with his own work, and hesitates to become involved in other areas without considering that his activities might have significant bearing also on them.

As a manager performs his managerial functions he should bear in mind that coordination is one of the desired by-products. When the manager plans he must immediately strive for coordination. As a matter of fact, the planning stage is the ideal time to bring about coordination, and you as a supervisor must see to it that the various plans within your department are properly interrelated. As a supervisor you should discuss these plans and alternatives with the workers who are to carry them out so that they have opportunity to express any doubts of synchronization and any objections. One of the overriding considerations in efficient planning is constant concern pertaining to coordination. This same concern for coordination should be prevalent when you as a manager organize. As a matter of fact, the purpose for setting up a structural framework as to who is to do what and when and where and how, is to obtain coordination; it is necessary in order to obtain the stated objective in a synchronized fashion. Whenever you group and assign activities and assign various subordinates to them the thought of coordination should be in your mind. By placing related activities which must be closely synchronized within the same area of authority, coordination will be facilitated. Coordination should be in the manager's mind when he performs his staffing function. You must make certain that you will have the right number of workers in the various positions to assure the proper performance of their functions. You should see to it that these employees are of such quality that they will be likely to coordinate their efforts. When you as a manager direct, you also are involved in coordination. As a matter of fact, the very essence of giving instructions means to coordinate the activities of the employees in such a manner that the overall objective of the institution will be reached in the most efficient way. You as a supervisor must continuously watch the progress of the different jobs under your direction in order to be sure that they are proceeding harmoniously. Last but not least, when the manager performs his controlling function, he is concerned with coordination. By controlling, the manager makes certain by means of checking and observing whether or not the activities are in conformance with the established goals and standards. If he finds any discrepancy he should take immediate remedial action so that whenever deviations have occurred, the situation can be remedied. By doing this he assures coordination at least from then on. The very nature of the controlling process is one that brings about coordination, the synchronized effort which, in the final analysis, will lead the organization and your department to the stated and desired objectives.

So you see that you as a manager, in performing your five managerial functions, should always have in your mind the overriding goal of achieving coordination, the synchronization of the efforts of all of your employees in your department. But not only must you as a supervisor be concerned with coordination within your own department, you as the supervisor have to coordinate the efforts of your entire department with the efforts of the other departments. This function of bringing about coordination with all the other divisions of the hospital or any other health care facility is a concern of the administrator. On the other hand, there is much that you also can do to facilitate coordination in this respect. However, our primary concern here is for you as a manager of your own department.

SUMMARY   The role of the supervisor is a most demanding one. To the employees in his department he represents management. Toward his own boss, the administrator, he is the subordinate. Toward the supervisors of other departments he must be a good colleague, coordinating his efforts with theirs to the achievement of the institution's objective. He must possess technical competence for the functions to be performed in his department and, at the same time, be a manager of that department. Management is a function of getting things done through people and with people. The way the supervisor handles the managerial aspect of his job will make the difference between running the department and being run by the department. The managerial aspects of the supervisory job are the same regardless of the function and regardless of the position within the administrative ladder. In his climb up the managerial ladder the managerial functions will increase, and the importance of the technical skills will gradually decrease. Managerial skills can be learned; a manager is not born. You can recognize a manager by the functions he performs and also by answering the question of whether or not he possesses authority. The managerial functions are: planning, organizing, staffing, directing, and controlling. But only if a man possesses authority will he be a manager. The power of authority will make his managerial job real. This authority is delegated to him by the superior manager, namely, the administrator. While authority is the key to the managerial job, the delegation of authority is the key to the creation of an organization. The overriding thought a manager must keep in mind while performing the managerial functions is the achievement of coordination, the synchronization of the efforts of all members of the organization toward the attainment of the objectives. Coordination will result as a by-product of the managerial functions. This is valid for all managerial jobs regardless of the particular function, the level within the administrative hierarchy, or the kind of enterprise you are connected with.

3

DECISION-MAKING

If you were to ask practicing managers to define in one or two words their main managerial function, they are very likely to reply that what permeates their job more than anything else is "making decisions." This problem of decision-making is in reality at the heart of all managerial functions. As a matter of fact, to make decisions is a substantial part of everybody's activities. All of us have to make decisions in many areas of endeavor. Therefore, decision-making and problem-solving should be something with which we are acquainted. However, very many of the problems with which we are confronted in our daily lives are frequently those with which we are thoroughly familiar and for which we have a pat answer. Solving these situations—these problems—does not usually cause us much difficulty. But when problems confront us which are of great magnitude and significance and cover areas with which we are not familiar we find it increasingly difficult to decide.

In your experience as supervisor of your department you are constantly called upon to find practical and basic solutions to problems which are caused by changing situations and unusual circumstances. Normally, you are in a position to arrive at a satisfactory conclusion. As a matter of fact, one reason why you are where you are is that you have made many more correct decisions than wrong decisions as the problems presented themselves. In reality, making decisions is something to which you are well accustomed. It is true that many of these decisions you have to make cover problems which arise out of the daily working situation; nevertheless, they are problems where you have to come to a conclusion as to what should be done. All managers go through—or at least should go through—the very same process of problem-solving or decision-making, the only difference being that the decisions to be made at the top of the administrative hierarchy are usually more far-reaching and affect more people and areas than those decisions which you have to make within your own department. But decision-making is a function which permeates the entire administrative hierarchy.

Of course, it must be kept in mind that once a decision has been made, effective action is necessary. Every decision made should be put into practice and it should be carried out. Obviously, there is nothing as useless as a good decision about which nobody does anything. But getting effective action is not the problem we are concerned with in this chapter. All our other chapters will be concerned mainly with ways in which the manager can achieve effective action. At the present time we will discuss the process which should come before action, the process you as a manager should go through in order to decide what action should be taken.

Often when we think of a man as a decision-maker a picture comes to our mind of an executive with horn-rimmed glasses bent over some papers, his pen in his right hand, ready to sign on the dotted line. Or the picture which comes to our mind is of a gentleman who in a meeting raises his right arm to vote one way instead of the other. All of these images have one point in common. They portray the decision-maker as a man at the very moment of choice when he is ready to follow the one or the other alternative which leads him from the crossroads. We are not concerned with this moment of decision-making. All of these images do not refer to the long, difficult process which must come before you reach the final moment of selecting one alternative over the other. It is this process, through which you should go before you decide on action, that we will discuss in the following.

As pointed out, decision-making is an important skill for managers to possess. And at the same time let us state that these skills involved in decision-making can be learned, and they can be taught just as the skills involved in playing tennis are taught. It has often been said that good decision-makers are born and not made. This kind of thinking is as wrong as that which we discussed in our first chapter when we explained that the managerial skills are learnable and trainable. Good decision-makers, like good athletes, are made and not born. Of course, each and every one is born with different physiological and biological potentialities. And everyone is born with an unequal amount of intelligence and many other differing characteristics and potentialities. A good decision-maker is made when a man with some natural endowment and intelligence develops these natural endowments into a mature skill by practice, learning, and effort. You, too, can learn how to make better decisions. This is doubly important because the task of making decisions holds true for the entire administrative organization. Your managerial job does not only involve making decisions yourself, but your job also involves seeing to it that those employees of the organization who work under you make decisions effectively. As a matter of fact, many of the daily decision-making activities for which you are responsible are to a great degree performed by those who work under your supervision. It is therefore not only necessary that you develop better decision-making skills for yourself, but that you also train your subordinates in this process of making decisions.

To make a decision means to cut off deliberation and to come to a conclusion. A decision is something that takes place prior to the actual performance of the action that has been decided upon. It is a conclusion that the manager has reached as to what he or others should do at some later time. In making a decision it is essential that the manager observe certain steps and follow these steps in the proper sequence: First, he must define the problem. After this, the problem must be analyzed; and after thorough analysis the manager should develop alternative solutions. Only after that can the manager decide upon the best solution. A discussion of these various steps follows.

DEFINITION OF THE PROBLEM   You have often heard supervisors say, "I wish I had the answer," or "I wish I had the solution to this," or he may say, "I wish I knew what to do about this." All of these questions indicate that the supervisor is overly concerned with having an *answer*. Instead of seeking the answer he should be looking for the problem. His first task is to find out what the problem is in the case in question; then he should work toward the solution, the answer. As someone has said, there really is nothing as useless as having the right answer to the wrong question. To define the problem, in most cases, is not an

24

easy task. What at times might appear to be the problem might be at best merely a symptom of the problem which shows on the surface. It is therefore necessary to dig deeper in order to locate the real problem and to define it. For example, it might seem that the supervisor is confronted with a problem of conflicting personalities within his department. Two of his employees are continually quarrelling and cannot get together. Upon checking into this situation the manager may find that in reality this is not a problem of personalities. He may discover that the problem is that he, as the manager, has never really defined the functions and duties of each employee, where these functions begin and where they end, and has never clarified where the other employee takes over. Therefore, what appeared on the surface to be a problem of personal conflict is actually a problem of an organizational, structural nature which is truly the supervisor's function to make clear. Only after he has realized the true nature of the problem can he do something about it, and the chances are good that once he clarifies the areas of activities between the two employees, the friction will stop.

There is little doubt that defining a problem in most instances is a time-consuming task, but it is time well spent. There is no need to go any further in the process of decision-making until you as a supervisor have clearly defined the problem.

ANALYSIS OF THE PROBLEM   After the problem—and not just the symptoms—has been defined, the manager can set about to analyze the problem. The first step in the analysis of the problem . is to assemble the facts. Getting the facts is often recommended as the first step in decision-making; but not until the problem has been defined does the manager know what information he really needs for a particular problem. Only after a clear definition of the problem can the supervisor decide how important certain data are and what additional information he may need. He will then gather as many facts as he possibly can.

Typical of most supervisory situations is the common complaint that more facts are needed. It is a complaint of the supervisor that he does not have all the facts he would like to have. This is often just an excuse to delay the making of the decision. You as a manager will never have *all* the facts available. There-

25

fore, it is necessary to make decisions on those facts which you do have available and also on those additional facts which you can get without too much delay and expense. Never will you have all the facts in the case.

At the same time it is wise to remember that what is considered a fact is to a certain degree colored by subjectivity. You should bear in mind that, after all, one cannot completely free oneself of the subjective element involved. As much as we want to exclude prejudice and bias, we are only human, and subjectivity will creep in somehow. Of course, we should make an effort to be as objective as possible in gathering and examining these facts. At the same time, in this process of analysis, the supervisor will do well to also think of intangible factors which may be involved. These are very difficult to assess and to analyze, but they do play a significant role. These intangibles are factors of reputation, morale, discipline, and considerations of this sort. It is exceedingly difficult to be specific about these items, but nevertheless, you should take them into consideration in the analysis of the problem on which you have to come to a decision.

DEVELOP ALTERNATIVES   After having defined and analyzed the problem, the manager's next step is to search for and develop various alternative solutions. You must make it an absolute rule that all possible alternatives should be taken into consideration. Always bear in mind that the decision you will finally make can only be as good as the best of the alternatives which you took into consideration. It can never be better than the best alternative you thought of. Therefore, if you have had many alternatives the likelihood is much greater that among them you also will have the best. It is almost unthinkable that a situation should not offer several alternatives. These alternate choices, however, might not always be obvious, and it is the duty of the manager to search for them. Also, some of them may not always be desirable; but different alternatives exist. The manager must force himself to search for and develop all possible alternative solutions. If he does not do this he is likely to fall into the "either-or" kind of thinking. You have often heard it said, after one minute's deliberation: "There is only one of two things we can do, namely, ... or ...." The manager is too easily inclined then to see only one of these two alternatives as the right one to follow. Nor is it enough for you as a supervisor to decide between the various alternatives with which you have been presented by your employees. The routine alternatives normally suggested by them may not include all the possible alternatives. It is your job as a manager to conceive of more and possibly better alternatives. There are several choices even in the most discouraging situations. None of the alternatives might be desirable but the manager still has a choice. Let us suppose that a business concern is in financial difficulties. The creditors have the choices of driving the enterprise into bankruptcy, agreeing to a moratorium to extend the payment of the bills for approximately a year, or compromising on a small percentage of the outstanding debts and clearing out the indebtedness. Here, in a most unpleasant situation, the creditors have three alternatives, none of which, of course, is desirable; but alternatives do exist and, therefore, there is a choice. The manager must make it an unchangeable rule that all kinds of alternatives must be developed before he starts his choice.

EVALUATION AND SELECTION FROM ALTERNATIVES (CHOICE)

As stated above, the purpose of decision-making is to select or choose from the various alternatives that specific one which will provide the greatest amount of wanted consequences and the smallest amount of unwanted consequences. After developing the alternatives the manager should test each of them by imagining that he has already put each into effect. He should try to foresee the probable desirable and undesirable consequences of each of these alternatives. After having thought them through and appraised their consequences he will then be in a position to compare the desirability of the various alternatives. In making this comparison as to which of the alternatives is more desirable than the other, the supervisor should bear in mind the degree of risk which is involved in each course of action. He must remain aware of the fact that there is no such thing as a riskless decision, and that one alternative will simply have more and the other less risk.

It is also possible that the question of timing will make one alternative preferable to the other alternative. After all, there

27

is a difference in how much time you have available and how much time is required to carry out one alternative in comparison to another. In this process of evaluating the different alternatives the supervisor should also bear in mind the resources, facilities, records, tools, and so on which are available to him. Furthermore, the manager should not forget to judge the different alternatives along the lines of economy of effort; in other words, which action will give the greatest result for the least amount of effort expended.

In those cases where one alternative clearly provides a greater number of desirable consequences and fewer unwanted consequences than any other alternative, then the decision of which alternative to choose is an easy one. However, the choice of the best alternative is not always so obvious. It is conceivable that at certain times two or more alternatives seem equally desirable. In such a case the choice is simply a matter of actual preference. It is also possible that the manager feels that no single alternative far outweighs any of the others or is sufficiently stronger. In this case it might be advisable to combine two of the better alternatives and make a compromise solution.

Sometimes a manager is confronted with a situation in which he finds that none of the alternatives is satisfactory and that all of them have too many undesirable effects. Or the manager might feel that none of the alternatives will bring about the desired results. In such a case the manager would do well to think of new alternative solutions.

You, as a supervisor, have also been in situations where the undesirable consequences of all the alternatives are so overwhelmingly bad that they practically paralyze the manager to the point where he will not take any action. At such a time the manager might feel that he always has one available solution to the problem, namely, to take no action at all. However, in so doing he is deceiving himself. The manager is wrong to believe that taking no action will get him "off the hook." Taking no action is as much a decision as the decision to take a specific action, although few people are aware of this. They feel that taking no action relieves them from making an unpleasant decision. The only way to avoid this is for the manager to visualize the consequences which will result from no action. The manager need only think through what would happen if no action is taken, and he will see that in so doing, he is in reality taking action.

Only when the manager forces himself to develop different alternatives will he be in a position to examine the probable outcome of each and every one of them. In so doing, he is very likely to find the one solution which will bring about the greatest number of wanted and the smallest number of undesirable consequences. Therefore, as we stated in the foregoing, the decision can only be as good as the best alternative taken into consideration.

EXPERIENCE In making his final selection from the various alternatives the manager is often influenced and guided by past experience. The chances are that history will repeat itself, and the old saying that experience is the best teacher still applies. There is no denying that the manager can often decide wisely because of his own experience or that of some other manager. Knowledge gained by past experience is a helpful guide and no manager should ever underestimate its importance. On the other hand, it is dangerous to follow past experience blindly.

Whenever the manager calls on experience as a basis for his choice between the alternatives he should examine the situation and the conditions which prevailed at the time of that particular decision. It may be that the conditions are still the very same which prevailed at that time, and thus the decision should be the same as was made on that previous occasion. More often than not, however, one will find that conditions have changed considerably and that the underlying circumstances and assumptions are no longer the same. Therefore, the decision should not be the same.

Previous experience can be very helpful, also, in the event the manager is called upon to substantiate the reasons for making a particular decision. This is a good defense tactic and many superiors use experience as valid evidence. But still there is no excuse for following experience blindly. Past experience must always be viewed with the future in mind. The underlying circumstances of the past, the present, and the future, must be considered. Only within this framework is experience a helpful approach to the selection from alternatives.

HUNCH AND INTUITION   Managers will at times admit that they based their decision on hunch and intuition. At first glance it might seem that some managers have an unusual ability for solving problems satisfactorily by intuitive means. However, a deeper search will disclose that the "intuition" on which the manager thought he had based his decision was only past experience or knowledge which he had stored away somewhere and called upon in order to come to a particular decision. In reality, the manager is recalling similar situations in which he has been involved in the past and which are stored in his memory; but he labels it "having a hunch." No superior would look favorably upon a subordinate who justifies the basis of his decisions as intuition or hunch. It is not a valid basis for the choice from alternatives.

EXPERIMENTATION   The avenue of experimentation is another approach to decision-making. In the scientific world where conclusions are reached by experiments in laboratories experimentation is essential. But in the area of managing, to experiment and to see what happens is, to say the least, too costly. There do exist certain instances where a limited amount of testing and experimenting is advisable. Such a situation may present itself in questions within your own department where you can at times undertake experimentation to a minor degree, as long as the consequences cannot be serious. There are some instances where a limited amount of testing may be advisable, and you may very well do so. In this small, restricted sense, experimentation may be valid. But, normally, in a managerial position, experimentation is at best a most expensive way of reaching a decision.

SCIENTIFIC DECISION-MAKING   There are, of course, other tools available to a manager for making decisions. When these are used the process is called scientific decision-making. It would not be advisable to burden you with scientific decision-making. Suffice it to say that for some overall managerial problems, managers often can call on the help of mathematicians, statisticians, and other types of scientists, who can bring their tools to bear on the existing problem. Normally, the problems a supervisor is confronted with are not of this magnitude. But if they should be of a mathematical or scheduling nature it might be helpful to discuss with the administrator the possibility of consulting some outside scientist for help in solving the particular problem.

SUMMARY   To reach a decision by facts, study, and analysis of various proposals is still the most generally approved avenue to the selection from alternatives. If an objective, rational, systematic way is used the manager is performing on a solid basis. The likelihood is good that you will make better decisions if you follow this systematic way of making decisions. First, you must define the problem. After you have defined it you must analyze the problem. Then you must develop all the alternatives you possibly can, think them through as if you had already put them into action, and consider the consequences of each and every one of them. Then you very likely can choose the one which has the greatest amount of wanted and least amount of unwanted consequences. In this process of choice you can often be aided by the past experience which you or some other manager has had. As long as you carry out the decision-making process in this manner you are on a solid basis. Not only can this be learned by you as a supervisor, but as a supervisor you can teach the same systematic step approach to your subordinates. In so doing you have the assurance that whenever they are confronted with a situation where they have to make a decision they will do it in a systematic way. Although this is not a guarantee for coming up with the best decisions always, it most certainly is more apt to produce better decisions than not.

4

COMMUNICATION

Your job as a supervisor is to plan, organize, direct, and control the work of the employees of your department and to coordinate their efforts, for the purpose of achieving the objectives laid out for your area of activities. But in order to achieve these you must explain and discuss the arrangement of the work. You must give directives. You must describe to each man what is expected of him. You will very likely need to speak to your employees regarding their performance. All of this is communication.

As you go on supervising your employees, you probably will come to realize that your skill in communication determines your success. Communication is the most effective tool you have for building and keeping a well functioning team. Just consider your own job, and you will quickly see why communication is essential to successful supervision. Is there any responsibility within your job which you as a supervisor could fulfill without communicating? Obviously not. Communicating is the most essential skill a supervisor must have. You know supervisors who are competent, technically knowledgeable and good mannered. Nevertheless, they do not seem to get anywhere. Deep down you probably know the reason: they cannot use words to sell themselves or to sell their plans; they cannot communicate. And in your career you also have observed those supervisors who have lost their skill in communication or who think that communication is no longer worth the effort. Before they knew it they had lost touch with their employees because they failed to communicate. The ability to communicate is absolutely essential to leadership. It is the only means you have as a supervisor to take charge of and train a group of employees, to direct them and to coordinate their activities so that the goal which you have pointed out can be reached. The problem of communication is vital for any organization. Without effective communication the superior-subordinate relationship cannot thrive.

GETTING EFFECTIVE COMMUNICATION
THE MEANING OF COMMUNICATION   Plainly stated, communication means the process of passing information and understanding from one person to another. Communication—fundamental and vital to all managerial functions—is a process of imparting ideas and of making oneself understood by others. The exchange is successful only when mutual understanding results. Since managing is getting things done through others, it is an obvious requirement that the manager communicate with the members of his group.

If you were to estimate it, you would find that you as a supervisor spend approximately ninety percent of your time in either sending or receiving information. It would be incorrect to assume that in all of these processes communication is really taking place. The mere fact that a supervisor is constantly engaged in sending and receiving messages is most certainly not any assurance that he is an expert in communicating. There is no need to point out to you the many instances where communication had not taken place: where the result was utter confusion and errors.

We define communication as a process of passing information and understanding from one person to another. The significant point here is that communication always involves two people, a sender and a receiver. It would be wrong to assume that communication is merely a matter of sending. There must be a receiver. One person alone cannot communicate; communication is not a one-way street. For example, a man who is stranded on a deserted island and who is shouting at the top of his voice does not communicate because he has no receiver. This is obvious. But this may not be so obvious to a manager who sends out a letter. Once he has mailed his letter he is inclined to believe that he has communicated. However, he has not communicated until and unless information and understanding has passed *between himself and the receiver.*

It should be noted that our definition of effective communication includes not only information but also understanding. The receiver may hear a sender because he has ears and still not understand what the sender means. Understanding is a personal matter between people. If the idea received by the receiver is the one which was intended, then we can say communication has taken place. If the idea received by the listener or reader is not the one which was intended, communication has not taken place; the sender has not communicated, he has merely spoken or written. It cannot be assumed that "simply telling" somebody is enough to guarantee successful communication. As long as there is no reception or an imperfect reception of the idea intended we cannot speak of having communicated.

All of us have been endowed with certain capacities for effective communication with others. Yet there are some supervisors who are much more effective as communicators than others. Communication is vital and it deserves your fullest attention. Your personal effectiveness will depend greatly on your ability to communicate. You must be able to transfer information and knowledge to your workers so that you are understood and that results are achieved. No subordinate can be expected to comply with a directive unless there is understanding on his part. Then again, the supervisor must know how to receive knowledge and understanding in the messages which are sent to him by his employees, by his fellow supervisors, and also by his boss.

Only through good communication can policies, procedures, and rules be formulated and carried out. Only with good communication can misunderstandings be ironed out, long-term and short-term plans achieved, and the various activities within a department coordinated and controlled. The success of all managerial functions depends on successful communication, and communication is a skill which can be acquired. All of us can improve our natural endowments to a great degree and become more effective communicators; in other words, better managers.

CHANNELS OF COMMUNICATION   In every organization the communication network has two distinct but equally important phases, namely, the official channel of communication and the informal channel, normally called the grapevine. Both channels carry messages from one person or group to another downward, upward, and sideward.

Formal communication channels are established mainly by the organization structure following the lines of authority from the administrator all the way down. You are familiar with the expression that messages and information must go through channels. The model of the formal channel of communication suggests that someone at the top issues a directive and the next person in the hierarchy passes the communication along to the men who report to him, and so on further down the line. The downward direction is the most frequently used and the one on which management relies most heavily for the communication. Downward communication helps to tie the different levels together and is used by the manager to communicate to subordinates directives, information, objectives, policies, procedures, and so forth.

Upward communication is a second but equally important direction of communication which flows through this official network. Any person who is charged with supervisory authority accepts an obligation to keep his own superior informed. Your subordinates must feel free to convey to you their opinions and attitudes and to report on activities and actions referring to their work. Management should encourage a free flow of upward communication, as this is the only means by which management can determine whether or not messages have been transmitted and received properly. Upward communication is the best way to determine whether or not proper action is taking place. Of course, there is much which you as a supervisor can do to assure this upward communication.

Generally speaking, downward communication starts action by subordinates. Its content is mostly of a directive nature, whereas upward communication is of an informative and reporting nature. As a supervisor, you should encourage and maintain the upward communication facilities and pay proper attention to the information transmitted. You as a supervisor must show that you want the facts and want them promptly. Unfortunately, the reaction of many managers is still very much like that of ancient tyrants who executed the "bearer of bad news." In your supervisory capacity you must encourage upward communication by a genuine desire to obtain and use the ideas suggested and reports from your subordinates, by being approachable, and by recognizing the importance of upward communication. Lack of an effective upward communication network will throttle the natural desire of your employees to communicate, will lead to frustration and will ultimately cause your employees to find different outlets.

In addition to downward and upward communication there is a third direction of communication which is essential for the efficient functioning of an enterprise. This is sideward or horizontal communication, which is concerned mainly with communication between departments or people on the same level but in charge of different functions. In order to achieve coordination between the various functions a free flow of horizontal communication is absolutely essential.

In addition to these official channels of communication there is the unofficial channel called the grapevine, which will be discussed at the end of this chapter.

Although it is essential to create, develop, and maintain channels of communication between the supervisor and his employees, it is more important to make certain that communication is actually achieved when information and ideas are sent along these channels. Therefore, our discussion here is mainly concerned with the essential elements of the communication process itself, the many barriers which prevent communication, and the ways and means you have available to overcome these obstacles. It is not sufficient to merely have good channels of communication. It is much more important that proper communication takes place.

ADEQUATE PREPARATION   The first step toward becoming a good communicator is to know exactly what you want. You must think the idea through until it becomes hard and solid in your mind—not just formless thoughts and desires you have not bothered to put into final form. Only if you understand your ideas can you be sure that another person will understand your instructions. Therefore, know what you want, and plan the sequence of those steps which are necessary to attain it. Study the subject until it is so clear in your own mind that you have no difficulty explaining it. In other words, do not start talking or writing before you know what you are going to say.

Also, before you begin to communicate, clarify in your own mind what you want to accomplish. If you want to make a job assignment, be sure that you have analyzed the job thoroughly so that you can explain it properly. If you are searching for facts, decide in advance what information you will need so that you can ask intelligent, pertinent and precise questions. If your discussion will entail a disciplinary problem, be certain that you have sufficiently investigated the case and have enough information before you reprimand or even penalize. Briefly speaking, take care that you do not start to communicate before you know what you are going to say and what you intend to achieve.

MEANS OF COMMUNICATION   The media for communication can be words, pictures, and actions. Words are, of course, the most important symbols used in the communication process. But it would be wrong to ignore the power of pictures in conveying meaning and understanding to other people. Pictures are visual aids and the manager will do well to resort to them from time to time. They are particularly effective if you use them in connection with well chosen words to complete a message. Business enterprises have made extensive use of pictures to communicate understanding in the form of blueprints, charts, drafts, models, posters, and so on. Motion pictures and the comic strips offer a clear proof of the power of pictures in communicating.

Action is another medium used in communication. The manager must not forget that what he *does* is interpreted by his subordinates, and his actions often speak louder than his words. The supervisor should realize that due to his managerial status, all observable acts communicate something to the employee whether he intended it to be so or not. Purposeful silence, gestures, a handshake, a shrug of the shoulder, a smile, all have meaning. For instance, a frown on someone's face may at times mean more than ten minutes of oral discussion or a printed page. By the same token the supervisor's inaction is a way of communication. It is very possible that unexplained action often communicates a meaning which was not intended. For example, some machinery or piece of equipment has been removed from the production floor without telling the workers the reason. To the workers, who may fear a threatened shutdown or move of the plant to another city, such unexplained action could communicate a meaning and a message which the manager had no intention whatsoever of sending.

SPOKEN AND WRITTEN WORDS   Of course, words are the medium most widely used in communication in today's "verbal environment." We all know that words can be tricky, and instructions that mean one thing to one employee may have a completely different meaning to someone else. You may remember the often told story about the maintenance foreman who asked the new worker to go out and paint the canopy in front of the building green. When the foreman checked on the job an hour later he found that the wastecan had been painted bright green. The new employee did not know what a canopy was. Perhaps he should have known. But no one had ever told him.

Words are used in both oral and written communications, and there is a place for both of them. It is, therefore, necessary that a supervisor be skilled in speaking, writing, listening, and reading. Although oral communication is the most frequently used, a well balanced communication system must pay due attention to both the written and oral media. As a supervisor you will not have too much occasion to use the written medium as most of your communication will take place by word of mouth. But there may be occasions where the supervisor will have to resort to written communication. In the following we are primarily referring to the spoken or oral communication.

In most instances oral communication is superior to the written medium, since communication by word of mouth normally achieves better ready understanding and saves time. This is so with oral telephone and oral face-to-face communication. As a matter of fact, in the supervisor's daily performance the man-to-man personal discussions between him and his subordinates are the principal two-way communication he uses. And the daily contacts are at the heart of an effective communication system. There is no form of written communication that can equal the oral communication between the supervisor and his employee. And even more effective than just oral communication, over the telephone or the public address system, is the oral face-to-face communication between the supervisor and his employee. Therefore, the effective supervisor will use this medium more than any other. The subordinate likes to see and hear his boss in person, and no written communication can be as effective as a personal meeting. Another reason for the greater effectiveness of oral communication is that most people can express themselves more easily and more completely by voice than by a letter.

Aside from this feature, the greatest single advantage of oral communication is that it provides an immediate feedback although the response may be only an expression on the person's face. By merely looking at the receiver the sender can judge how he is reacting to what is being said. Oral communication will enable the sender to find out immediately what the receiver is hearing and what he does not hear. Oral communication enables the recipient to ask questions right there and then if the meaning is not clear, and the sender can explain his message and clarify unexpected problems raised by the communication. The manner and tone of the human voice can impart the message with meaning and shading which even long pages of written words simply cannot convey. The manner and tone create the atmosphere of communication and the response is influenced accordingly.

Inasmuch as oral communication is the most effective and the most frequently used tool of the supervisor to get his job done, it is of utmost importance that he become a skilled communicator. The good communicator must know how to speak effectively and be aware of his listener. He must be familiar with the many barriers to effective communication which may plug the communication lines. He must know how to overcome these barriers and how to unplug the pipeline. The effective communicator must know that the speaker and the listener are two separate individuals who live in different worlds and that there are many factors which can interfere and play havoc with the message that passes between them. Always remember that there is no communication until and unless the meaning which is received by the listener is the same which the sender intended to send. Indeed, there are a large number of reasons why communications break down. Therefore, we turn to those considerations which often create a roadblock to communication, and then we shall discuss ways and means of successfully overcoming them.

ROADBLOCKS TO COMMUNICATION

Always bear in mind that the sender and the receiver of a communication are two separate individuals living in different worlds. Due to this difference there are many barriers which can easily distort the messages between them with the result that the meaning given to the message by one person may not be what the sender intended it to be. All of you are familiar with the misunderstandings, frictions, and inconveniences that arise when communications break down. These breakdowns are not only costly in terms of money, but they also create misunderstandings which hurt your teamwork and morale. Many of your supervisory problems are due to faulty communication. The way you as a supervisor communicate with your subordinates is the essence of your relationship, and most problems of human relations grow out of poor communication, and even the lack of communication. Therefore, it is important for you to be familiar with some of the more important barriers which cause breakdowns and misunderstandings in communication. After we have discussed them we shall see what you can do in order to overcome these barriers.

LANGUAGE BARRIER   As stated above, words often are tricky. Normally, words serve well and people understand each other. But it sometimes happens that the same word may suggest different meanings to different people. In such a case the words themselves create a barrier to communication. You have often heard it said that people on different levels "speak a different language." There are many instances where a frustrating conversation ends with the admission that "we are just not talking the same language." And both have been conversing in English. Therefore, in order to avoid a breakdown in communication the communicator should use the language of the listener and not his own language. He should speak a language which the receiver is used to and which he understands. It is not a question of whether he *ought* to understand it; the question is, simply, does he? He ought to use plain, simple words. The supervisor should employ plain, direct, uncomplicated language.

Of course, this is difficult at times because the English language assigns several meanings to one word. For example, the word "round" has many meanings. We speak of round as a ball—he walks round and round—a round dozen of eggs—a round trip—a round of beef—round as a cylinder, etc., etc. In such an instance make certain that you clarify the meaning of a rather common word. Always bear in mind that the listener tends to listen and to interpret the language based on his own experience.

BARRIERS DUE TO STATUS AND POSITION   It cannot be denied that the organization structure, with its various levels in the administrative hierarchy, creates a number of status levels among the members of your enterprise. Status refers to the regard and attitude which is displayed and held toward a position and its occupant by the members of the organization. There is no denying that there is a difference between the level of the administrator and that of the supervisor, and between the level of your employees and your own as a supervisor. This difference in status and position becomes apparent as one level communicates with the other.

When an employee listens to the message from his supervisor several factors become operative. First of all, the receiver evaluates what he hears in relation to his own position, background, and experience; he also takes the sender into account. It is difficult for the receiver to separate what he hears from the feelings he has about the person who sends the message. It therefore happens often that in so doing he adds nonexistent motives to the sender. Union members are often inclined to interpret a management's statement in the most uncomplimentary manner possible due to the fact that often they are convinced that management is trying to weaken and undermine the union. Such a mental block does not make for good understanding.

The supervisor must realize that status and position influence feelings and prejudices, and thus create barriers. He can overcome these barriers by putting himself in the employee's position and by analyzing and anticipating his reaction before he sends the message. Not only does the subordinate evaluate the boss's words differently, but he often places undue importance upon a superior's gesture, silence, smile, or other facial expression. Simply speaking, the boss's words are not just words; they are words that come from a boss.

41

Similar obstacles due to status and position also arise in the upward flow of communication since the subordinate is eager to appear favorably in his boss's eyes. Therefore, he conveniently and protectively screens the information which he passes up the line. A subordinate, therefore, is likely to tell his superior what the latter likes to hear and will omit or soften what is unpleasant. And by the same token the subordinate is anxious to cover up his own weaknesses when talking to a person in a higher position. A supervisor often fails to pass on important information because he believes that such information would reflect unfavorably on his own supervisory abilities. You can imagine that after two or three successive protective screenings of this sort the message is likely to be considerably distorted.

BARRIERS DUE TO RESISTANCE TO CHANGE Most people prefer things as they are and do not welcome changes in their working situation. Therefore, this natural resistance to change can constitute serious barriers to communication. Very often the message intends to convey a new idea to the subordinate, something which will change either his work assignment, his position, or something close to his daily routine. This inclination to resist change is due to the natural inclination of people to leave the existing environment in the present equilibrium in which they find themselves. Ultimately each and every one lives in his own little world; although it may not be a perfect world, he sooner or later learns to make peace with it and to live within it more or less happily. Consequently, a message which will change this equilibrium is greeted with suspicion and the listener's receiving apparatus works just like a filter, rejecting new ideas if they conflict with what he already believes. He is likely to receive only that portion which confirms his present belief, and ignore anything that conflicts. Sometimes his filters work so efficiently that in reality he does not hear at all. Even if he should hear he will either reject it as false or he will find some convenient way of twisting its meaning to fit his preconceived ideas. Ultimately the receiver hears what he wishes to hear. If the listener is insecure, worried, and fearful in his position this barrier becomes even more powerful.

You as a supervisor have often been confronted with situations where you noticed that the listener only half listened to what you had to say. Your employee is so busy and preoccupied with his own thoughts that he tends to give attention only to those ideas he hopes to hear. He simply selects only those parts of the total communication which he can readily use. Those bits of information which he does not care for or are irreconcilable are just conveniently brushed aside, not heard at all, or easily explained away. This constitutes serious barriers to communication. You as a supervisor must be aware of these possibilities, particularly when the message you intend to convey contains some change, a new directive, or anything which could conceivably interfere with his routine or working environment. But only if you are aware of such possible reactions can you anticipate the difficulties which will result if these barriers block effective communication. This is why it is important for you to be familiar with the usual manner in which your subordinate reacts toward any change.

ADDITIONAL BARRIERS TO COMMUNICATION In addition to the above-mentioned roadblocks there are many others which arise from specific situations. There are obstacles due to emotional reaction, such as deep-rooted feelings and prejudice, to physical conditions, and many other barriers of diversified origin. It may be indifference, the "don't care" attitude, which stands in the way of communication. In this instance the message may get through all right, but is acted on only half-heartedly or not at all. There may be complacency on the subordinate's part which prevents the message from getting across. All of these and many others form serious roadblocks to clear communication. Unless the supervisor is familiar with them he is in no position to overcome them.

Every supervisor is familiar with the misunderstandings, frictions, and inconveniences which result when communication breaks down. No manager should just assume that the message which he sends will be received as it was intended. However, since the effectiveness of the supervisory job depends largely on the accurate transmission of information and orders, the manager must do all within his power to overcome these barriers and to improve communication.

43

MEANS FOR OVERCOMING BARRIERS TO COMMUNICATION

FEEDBACK   Among the several methods available to improve communication, feedback is probably the most important one. The sender must be on the alert for some signal or clue indicating whether or not he is understood. Merely asking the receiver and getting simply "yes, sir" as an answer in most instances is not enough reassurance. Most of the time more than this is required in order to make sure that the message was actually received as it was intended.

The simplest way to do this is to observe the receiver and judge his responses by non-verbal clues such as expression of bewilderment or understanding, facial expressions such as the raising of an eyebrow or a frown. This kind of feedback is, of course, only possible in face-to-face communication, and it is one of the outstanding advantages of face-to-face oral communication. Then again, the sender may ask the receiver to repeat in his own words the information he has just transmitted. This is much more satisfactory than merely asking him whether or not he understood or if the instruction is clear. If the receiver states in his own words the content of the message then the sender will really know what the receiver has heard, and what he did or did not understand. At that time the employee may ask additional questions and request comment which the supervisor can provide right there and then. This direct feedback is probably the most direct and useful way to make certain that the message has gotten across. Without being aware of it, you as a supervisor have probably been using this principle of feedback in your daily communication.

DIRECT AND SIMPLE LANGUAGE   Another helpful means to overcome roadblocks in communication is for the manager to use words which are understandable and as simple as possible. Long, technical, and complicated words should be avoided. The sender should use language which the receiver actually will understand and not the language which he ought to understand. The question is not whether he should have understood it, but, rather, did he understand it?

EFFECTIVE LISTENING   One means for overcoming the barriers to communication is for the sender to take more time for listening. Give the other party a chance to tell what is on his mind. The only way you can convince the other party of your interest in him and your respect for his opinions is to listen to him and to hear them. The supervisor who pays attention and listens to what the subordinate is saying learns more about him and more about his job. By listening to the subordinate, the supervisor will learn about the employee's values and relationships to his working environment. There is no need to agree, but there is a great need for the supervisor to try to understand the other person. It may be advisable to state from time to time what has been expressed by asking the common question, "Is this what you mean?" The listener must be patiently listening to what the other person has to say even though he may believe it to be unimportant. Listening will greatly improve communication since it will reduce misunderstandings. By listening, the speaker can adjust his message to fit the responses and the world of his receiver. This opportunity to do so is also an advantage of the oral communication over the written messages.

Much of the difficulty in listening is caused by the fact that the speed of thought moves several times faster than the speed of speech. It is too easy for the listener to let his mind wander and daydream. The listener should make an effort to use the idle time for thinking, to use the lag between speech and thought to concentrate on what is being said. The listener can do this by summarizing in his mind what the speaker has said, to try to read the thoughts behind the words and to look ahead of what may be said. The fact that the mind is working on what the other party is saying improves the listening skill. One of the worst things a listener can do is to sit with faked attention while his mind is on a mental excursion and daydreaming. Only by tuning in to the world and thinking of the other party can the supervisor get his message across.

ACTIONS SPEAK LOUDER THAN WORDS   The manager who fails to bolster his talk with action fails in his job as a communicator no matter how capable he is with words. The supervisor must realize that he communicates by his actions as much as he communicates by his words. As a matter of fact, actions speak louder than words. Therefore, one of the best ways to give meaning to the message is to behave accordingly. The supervisor must realize that due to his superior position often he is the center of attention to his employees, and he communicates through all observable actions regardless of whether or not this is what the supervisor intended. If the verbal announcements are backed up by action it will help the supervisor overcome barriers to communication. However, if the manager says one thing but does another, sooner or later his employees will "listen" primarily to what he "does."

BE REDUNDANT   In order to overcome barriers to communication it is frequently advisable for a supervisor to repeat the message a few times, preferably using different words. The degree of redundancy will depend largely upon the content of the message and the experience and background of the employee. On the other hand, the sender must caution himself not to be so repetitious that the message may be ignored because it sounds familiar. In case of doubt, a degree of repetition is safer than none.

THE SUPERVISOR'S DUTY FOR UPWARD COMMUNICATION

Every person who has been put into a supervisory position accepts an obligation to keep his own boss informed. As we stated at the outset, the supervisor is the man in the middle. He is not only responsible for good communication downward to his workers and his employees, but he is also responsible for good communication upward to keep his own boss up-to-date and well informed. Most supervisors will agree with the statement that it is much easier for them to "talk down" than to "speak up." Most supervisors will agree with this statement especially if they have ever had to tell their boss that they did not meet a certain schedule due to bad planning or that they forgot to carry out an order.

It is the supervisor's job to keep his boss advised of up-to-date facts concerning the supervisor's department. The supervisor should inform his superior of any significant developments and he should inform him as soon as possible after they occur. It would be most unfortunate if the boss were to learn about this news elsewhere, because this would indicate that he is not on top of his job. You as a supervisor have the duty to keep him up to date even if the information concerns errors that have occurred. It is his right to have complete information, and it is your duty to provide complete information to him about the functioning of your department. After all, he is still responsible if anything goes wrong.

Upward communication should be passed on promptly and in a complete and accurate form. Your superior may have to act on what you tell him. Therefore, the information must get to him in time and in a form which will enable him to take the necessary action. Therefore, assemble as many facts as you need to assemble and check them carefully before you pass them on to your boss. Try to be as objective as possible. This, of course, will be quite difficult at times since subordinates want to appear favorable in the eyes of the boss. There is a danger that you may soften the information a bit so that things will not look quite so bad in his eyes as they actually are. Always bear in mind that sooner or later any malfunctioning is discovered. Therefore, when difficulties arise it is best to tell your superior what the score is even if this means admitting mistakes on your part. Always keep in mind that your boss depends on the supervisor for the upward communication just as you depend on your employees to pass their bits of information and action on to you.

THE GRAPEVINE, THE UNOFFICIAL CHANNEL OF COMMUNICATION

At the beginning of this chapter it was briefly indicated that the communication network has, besides the formal channels of communication, an informal network of communication commonly referred to as the grapevine. The grapevine is a natural outgrowth of the informal organization and the social interaction of people and their natural desire to communicate with each other. It must be looked upon as a perfectly natural activity. The grapevine fulfills the subordinate's desire to be "in the know" and to be kept posted on the latest information. The grapevine gives the members of the organization an outlet for their imagination and an opportunity to relieve their apprehensions in the form of rumors. At the same time it offers to the supervisor excellent insight into what the subordinates think and feel. An efficient manager will acknowledge the grapevine's presence and will put it to good use if possible. The news which the grapevine carries consists at times of factual information, but most of the time it carries inaccurate information, half truths, rumors, private interpretations, suspicions, and other various bits of distorted information. It is active all day long and is a part of the natural organizational life. It spreads information with amazing speed and often faster than most official channels could.

The grapevine has no definite pattern or stable membership. Its path and behavior cannot be predicted, and the path followed yesterday is not necessarily the same as today and tomorrow. Most of the time only a small number of employees will be active participants in the grapevine. The vast majority of the employees hear of the information through the grapevine but do not pass it along. Any person within your organization is likely to become active in the grapevine at one occasion or the other. There are, of course, some subordinates who tend to be more active than others. They feel that their prestige is enhanced by providing the latest news, and thus do not hesitate to spread and change the news as to its "completeness" and "accuracy." Since the receiver knows that the sender cannot be held accountable, it is understandable that all participants exercise a considerable degree of imagination whenever they pass on the information. The grapevine, in the form of rumors, gives the members of the organization an outlet for ridding themselves of their apprehensions. It serves as a safety valve for the emotions of the subordinates, providing them with the means to freely say what they please without the danger of being held accountable.

The grapevine often carries a good amount of useful information in addition to distortions, rumors and half truths. If properly used it helps clarify and disseminate formal communication. It often spreads information which could not be disseminated through the official channels of communication.

The manager should accept the fact that he can no more eliminate the grapevine than he can abolish the informal organization. It is unrealistic to expect that rumors can be stamped out; the grapevine is bound to exist in every organization. In order to be able to deal with it the supervisor must tune in on the grapevine and learn what the grapevine is saying. He must learn who the leaders are and who is likely to spread the information. The wise supervisor will learn how to live with it and to make good, constructive use of the inevitable.

If you look for the causes of rumors you will probably find that rumors often begin in the wishful thinking of anticipation, or that rumors are created by uncertainty and fear or simply by malice and dislike. It is quite common that if an employee wants something badly enough, suddenly he starts passing the word. For instance, if an employee wants a raise, he may start the rumor that management will give an across-the-board raise. Nobody knows for certain where or how it started, but the story spreads like wildfire. Everyone wants to believe it. Of course, it is bad for the morale of a group to build up their hopes in anticipation of something that will not happen. If such a story is getting around which the supervisor realizes will lead to disappointment, he ought to move quickly to debunk it by presenting the facts. A straight answer is almost always the best answer. The best prescription for the cure of rumors of this type is to expose the facts.

Another frequent cause for rumors to start is fear. If in an enterprise the activities slack off and management is forced to lay off some of the employees, stories quickly multiply. In periods of insecurity and great anxiety the grapevine will become more active than at other occasions. Usually the rumors are far worse than what actually happens. Here, again, it is better to give the facts than to conceal them. If the supervisor does not disclose the facts the employees will make up their own "facts" and they usually are worse than reality. In many instances much of this fear was created by uncertainty which can be eliminated if the facts of what will happen are disclosed. Continuing rumors and uncertainty are likely to be more demoralizing than even the saddest facts.

Rumors often are started simply by dislike, anger and malice. Here again, the best prescription is to come out with the facts if this is possible. Of course, at times this will be quite difficult, and the best way to stop a rumor peddler is to expose him and

49

the untruthfulness of the statement. The superior should always bear in mind that the receptiveness of any group to the rumors of the grapevine is directly related to the strength of the supervisor's leadership. If your employees believe in your fairness and good supervision they will quickly debunk any rumor once you have exposed the facts or given your answer to it.

Nevertheless, there is no way to eliminate the grapevine; even with the best channels of communication, an organization without the grapevine in unthinkable. The manager, therefore, will do well to listen to it and develop his skill in dealing with it. As a good manager you will know that certain events will cause an undue amount of anxiety. If this is so, then explain immediately why changes are taking place, why orders are being given, and so on. When emergencies occur, when changes are introduced, when policies are changed, explain why. Otherwise your subordinates will make up their own explanations and often they will be incorrect. There are situations, however, where you as a supervisor do not have the correct facts either. In such instances let your superiors know what is bothering your employees. Ask your superior for specific instructions as to what information you may give, how much you may tell, and when. Also, when anything happens which might cause rumors, meet with your chief assistants and lead employees. Give them the story and guide their thinking. They then can spread the facts before anyone else can spread the rumors.

5

AUTHORITY, RESPONSIBILITY, AND DELEGATION

As a supervisor you are part of management. You have been given authority by your own boss to manage the affairs of your department. In the following discussion we will explain the meaning of authority. We will discuss such questions as what to do with authority once you have it, where, when, and how to apply or withhold it. You are probably aware of the fact that many competent supervisors seldom have to "use" their authority. They find it unnecessary to "throw their weight around" when giving orders and instructions. Although a good supervisor will try to minimize the occasions when he has to resort to authority, he cannot altogether abandon authority. There are times when he must act as a boss. As a matter of fact, there are some people who expect their boss to provide "firm" leadership. In any event, it is essential for a good supervisor to know how to use authority because the way in which it is used will make the difference between resentment and acceptance.

AUTHORITY

Before we can go into these aspects, it is essential for a supervisor to become familiar with what this concept of authority really means and from where it stems. As stated before, authority is the key to the managerial job. Authority is the power to request your subordinates to do a certain thing or to refrain from doing so. In the final analysis, and as a last resort, the manager has the power to take disciplinary action in the event the subordinate should refuse to do as he is told. This, of course, is the least desirable practice and such action should not be relied on in the daily activities. A successful supervisor knows that in order to induce his employees to perform the required duties willingly and enthusiastically it is best not to invoke authority, but to utilize other ways and means to get the job done. As a matter of fact, in reality it has come to the point where most supervisors do not even speak of authority at any time. It is essential, nevertheless, for you to know what it really means if you should have to use it. Of course, as stated before, there are much better ways of exercising one's authority than to discipline or even to dismiss one of your employees. All of this will be discussed fully later on. But bear in mind that the point made here is that the supervisor must have authority in order to be a manager. Without it his job is not real. Without authority only chaos would result.

FORMAL ORIGIN   You can trace the origin of your authority as coming directly from your boss who has delegated it to you. He, in turn, receives his authority, let us say, from the associate administrator who, in turn, receives his authority from the administrator who, in turn, traces his authority directly back to the governing board. In private profit-making corporations the ultimate source of authority lies with the stockholders, loosely speaking, the owners of the corporation. This is the formal way of looking at the origin of authority as a power which is the result of our recognition of private property. The owners delegate this power to those whom they have put into managerial positions to administer the affairs of the undertaking. From the top administrator it flows down through the channel of command until it reaches the supervisor. This way of looking at authority is considering the source of authority in the formal way.

ACCEPTANCE ORIGIN   The foregoing is the realistic way to look at the source of your authority but, on the other hand, at times you may wonder if you can rely solely on this power if it is derived through this process of delegation from the top on down. If you have not experienced such an incident, you may have heard the following story which has been repeated in many shops. A heated discussion occurred between the foreman and one of his men concerning an order which had been given. When the discussion grew into a bitter quarreling, the foreman finally shouted, "Jack, you are fired!" Jack, however, in the same heated manner, replied, "You can't fire me. I quit." It is obvious what happens to Jack. He is no longer with the company regardless of whether or not the foreman had fired him or if he had quit the job. But this remark of Jack's, "You can't fire me. I quit," caused the supervisor to become concerned about the significance of his authority. Events of this type bring out the fallacy of depending on the sheer weight of authority. Many managers believe that unless your employees accept your authority you, as a manager, actually do not possess authority. In reality, employees often have little choice left between accepting authority or not accepting it. The only choice the subordinate obviously has is to leave the job. However, this is a worrisome thought, and there is no doubt that there is some merit to the way of looking at authority as something which must be accepted by your workers. In many instances you do not have a real problem since an employee, when he accepts a job, knows that the boss of the department has the authority to give orders, to take disciplinary action, and to do whatever goes with his managerial position.

Briefly stated, the origin of authority can be considered from two viewpoints, namely, the formal way of looking at authority as something which originates with private property—formally handed down from the top to the lowest line supervisor, and, in contrast, authority as something which is conferred upon the supervisor by his subordinates' acceptance of his authority. It is not our intention to go further into this academic argument. We have touched on it briefly, however, because in reality it weighs heavily in the practice of supervision. Knowing about the different ways of looking at authority will enable you to exercise it in the best possible manner. But at the same time you must be aware that you possess it and, if need be, can resort to it as a final recourse. Obviously, no supervisor in this day and age would want to rely on his weight of authority to motivate his workers to perform their jobs. However, there will be times and occasions when the supervisor has to resort to authority. There are occasions when he must act as a boss and there are situations where he will have to make full use of his authority and power. But these will be the exceptions and not the rule. Therefore, he must be familiar with the content and the meaning of authority. And even then, when he has to invoke and rely on his authority the manner in which he will apply it will make a difference in whether his position will be resented or accepted. There will be decisions which the subordinate dislikes. This cannot be helped at the time. But the prudent manner in which the supervisor invokes his authority will make the difference between his being resented or accepted as a fair supervisor.

LIMITS OF AUTHORITY Regardless of whether the concept of authority is considered from the formal point of view or from the theory of acceptance, there are definite limitations to the concept of authority, either explicit or implied. Some of these limitations stem from internal and others from external sources. Authority is limited by such restrictions as our codes, folkways, and laws; and over a period of time many political, legal, ethical, social, and economic considerations have put limitations on the concept of authority. The articles of incorporation set limits to the authority of the administrator. The by-laws may place further restrictions on the administrator's authority. There are many laws which clearly limit the authority of a manager. In addition to this, each manager in a particular position is subject to specific authority limitations spelled out by the administrator in the assignment of his duties and delegation of authority. Generally speaking, there are more limitations on the scope of authority the further down one goes in the managerial hierarchy. The lower down in the administrative hierarchy, the more restrictions on the authority.

In addition to all of the above, there are a number of other limitations. There are biological restraints simply because the human being does not have the capacity to do certain things. No subordinate can be expected to do the impossible. In addition to these restraints there are physical, psychological, and even economic limitations to the concept of authority. In today's society considerations of this kind significantly limit the scope of authority of every manager and supervisor.

DELEGATION OF AUTHORITY

Just as authority is the key to the managerial job, so is delegation of authority the key to the creation of an organization. Delegation of authority means the granting of enough power to subordinates to operate within prescribed limits. Only by delegating authority to subordinate managers is an organization created. The delegation of authority makes organization possible. Through this process of delegation the subordinate manager receives his authority from his boss. But delegation of authority does not mean that the boss surrenders all of his authority. The delegating manager still retains his overall authority, as a matter of fact, to such a degree that he can, if need be, revoke all or part of whatever authority he has granted to a subordinate manager. A good comparison can be made between delegating authority and imparting knowledge in school. The teacher in school shares knowledge with his students who then possess the knowledge; but the teacher also retains the knowledge.

In the process of delegation, authority is distributed throughout the organization. It flows downward from the source of all authority at the top, through the various levels of management to the supervisor, and from him possibly to his foremen and lower line supervisors. There is a clear line from the ultimate source of authority to the lowest managerial ranks in the organization. This chain of command must be clearly understood by every subordinate, and must be closely adhered to or else the risk exists of undermining authority. It is quite possible that by the time this "flow of authority" reaches you as a supervisor it has pretty well narrowed down to a discreet "trickle" instead of a broad flow or continuous stream of delegation. Nevertheless, it can be traced directly upward to the ultimate source.

THE THREE COMPONENTS OF DELEGATION   This process of delegation which is the lifeblood of an organization is something with which every supervisor must be thoroughly familiar. It consists of three components all of which must be present. They are inseparably related in such a manner that a change in one of these three will require adjustment of the other two. The three aspects of this process of delegation are: 1) assignment of duties by a manager to his immediate subordinate; 2) the granting of permission (authority) to make commitments, use resources, and take all actions which are necessary to perform these duties; and 3) the creation of an obligation (responsibility) on the part of each subordinate to perform the duties satisfactorily. Unless all three are present and coextensive the success of the delegating process cannot be insured. As a matter of fact, any change in one of the three aspects will require adjustment of the other two. The following is a discussion of each of these three components of the process of delegation.

ASSIGNMENT OF DUTIES   In the assignment of duties the manager determines how the work in his department is to be divided among his subordinates. He will consider the best way for the various jobs to be done, and assigns them accordingly. In checking the jobs and duties in the department the manager will examine all of them to see which of them he can assign to someone else and which cannot be assigned to a subordinate. There are some duties which are routine, and there is no doubt that the manager can assign all of these to his subordinates. There are other functions to be performed which he can assign only to those subordinates who are particularly qualified for them. And then there are some functions which a supervisor cannot delegate and must do himself. The way in which the supervisor will assign the jobs to his employees is of great significance, and much of the success of the manager will depend on this. This function of the supervisor will be discussed further throughout this text. Let it be sufficient at this time to say that the first consideration in the process of delegation of authority is that a certain task or duty must be assigned to your subordinate; he must have a job to perform.

GRANTING OF AUTHORITY   The second aspect in the process of delegation is the granting of authority, the granting of permission to make commitments, to use resources, and to take all those steps which are necessary to the successful performance of the allocated duties. The granting of authority means that you confer upon your subordinate the right and power to act and to make decisions within a pre-determined limited area. It is necessary for the manager to determine the scope of authority which is to be delegated. How much authority can be delegated, of course, depends on the amount of the authority the manager himself possesses. The degree of authority is also related to the job to be done. Generally speaking, enough authority must be granted to the subordinate for him to adequately and successfully perform what is expected of him. There is no need for the degree of authority to be larger than necessary; but by all means it must be sufficient to get the job done. If you expect your employee to fulfill the task which you have assigned to him and to make reasonable decisions for himself within this area, he must have enough authority to do all of this. He does not need to have additional authority which is not necessary; but there should be enough for him to make use of all the resources he will need.

You as a supervisor must be specific in telling him what authority he has and what he can do. It is much better to be clear instead of letting your employee guess how far his authority may go. If you do not state this clearly he may wonder how far his authority will extend and experiment by trial and error. You as a supervisor may have found yourself in this deplorable position where your own boss was not explicit as to how much authority you really had. He would not commit himself when you asked him and you were left to trial and error methods. You did not know how far you could go and, all in all, it was a frustrating situation. You do not want this to happen to your subordinates. Therefore, be as clear as possible regarding the degree of authority which they have in performing the jobs you request them to do. As time goes on, of course, they will know, and less explanation will be necessary in the performance of their daily work. But bear in mind that the granting of authority must always be sufficient to get the job done. If you should change a job assignment of your employee, at the same time check the degree of authority you have given him to make certain that it is still appropriate. Perhaps it is more than he needs. Then you should clarify this also. But whenever you change the job, at the same time you must reconsider the degree of authority he should have.

Only one boss Throughout this process of delegation your employee must be reassured that all his orders and all authority can come only from you, as the only boss he has. The delegation of authority, issuance of orders, must come only from a single supervisor to the employee, and each employee reports to only one supervisor. This is what is known as the principle of unity of command, and it is one of the most widely recognized principles of management. But situations occur where two superiors try to delegate authority to one subordinate. Ever since biblical times it has been pointed out that it is difficult, if not impossible, to serve two masters. It is bound to lead to unsatisfactory performance by the employee, and it results in confusion of authority. The subordinate does not know which of the two bosses has that authority which will contribute most toward his success and progress with the organization. Having only one superior to whom to report will eliminate conflicts of this sort. You may have observed instances where this basic principle of unity of command—having one boss—was disregarded and violated in practice. Eventually such situations resulted in conflicts and organizational difficulties. Therefore, you must make certain that there is only one boss who can give orders to the employee.

RESPONSIBILITY   The third major aspect of the delegation of authority is the creation of an obligation on the part of the subordinate toward his boss to satisfactorily perform the assigned duties. The acceptance of this obligation creates responsibility. This creating of responsibility is the third aspect of the process of delegation, and without it delegation is not complete. The terms responsibility and authority are closely related to each other. The term responsibility, just as the term authority, has often been misunderstood and misused. It is common practice to use expressions such as "keeping subordinates responsible," "carrying out a responsibility," etc. Responsibility is the obligation of a subordinate to perform the duty as required by his superior. By accepting a job, by accepting the obligation to perform the assigned duties, the employee implies acceptance of his responsibility. It results from a contractual agreement in which the employee agrees to perform his duties in return for rewards. The responsibility is an obligation which is exacted from the subordinate to accomplish these duties. It is essential to bear in mind that responsibility cannot be delegated. It cannot be shifted. Responsibility is something which your subordinate accepts. The supervisor can delegate to a subordinate the authority to perform and to accomplish a specific job. But he does not delegate responsibility in the sense that once duties are assigned the supervisor is relieved of the responsibility for them. The delegation of tasks does not relieve the supervisor from his own responsibilities for these duties. A manager can delegate authority to his subordinate, but he cannot delegate any of his responsibility.

It is true that the administrator of a hospital and related health facilities must delegate to his assistant or associate administrators the authority to perform various tasks and services. They, in turn, of necessity have to delegate a large portion of their authority to the supervisors below them; but none of them delegates any responsibility. Responsibility is the obligation of a subordinate to perform the tasks assigned. It is an obligation which is owed to one's boss. This obligation cannot be shifted or reduced by assigning duties to another. When you as a supervisor are called upon by your boss to explain the performance within your department you cannot plead as a defense that you have "delegated the responsibility" for such activity to some employee of your group. You have remained responsible, and you must answer to your boss. Regardless of the extent to which you as a supervisor create an obligation on the part of your employees to perform satisfactorily, you retain the ultimate responsibility along with your authority.

This may be a worrisome thought for you. The fact remains that although responsibility is something which you accept you cannot rid yourself of it. No doubt reality must be taken into account. After all, delegations and re-delegations are necessary to get the job done. Although you as a supervisor will exercise the best managerial practices, you cannot be certain that each and every one of your subordinates will use his best judgment. Therefore, allowances must be made for errors, and in appraising your performance as a supervisor some attention will be paid to the degree to which you as a supervisor must depend on your subordinates to get the job done. Although the responsibility has remained with you, your boss will understand that you have to depend on your employees. In appraising your performance he will take into consideration how much care you have taken in the selection of the employees, in training them and supervising them thoroughly, and in controlling their activity. Although the responsibility has not been shifted away from you, your boss should take all of these matters into consideration when he appraises your own performance.

EQUALITY OF THE THREE COMPONENTS Always bear in mind that the three components must go together in order to make the process of delegation of authority successful. There must be enough authority granted to your subordinate to do the job. The responsibility which you can expect him to accept cannot be more than the area of authority which you have granted him. Your subordinates cannot be expected to accept responsibility for activities for which you have not handed them any authority. In other words, do not "keep your subordinates responsible" for something for which you have not granted authority. Also bear in mind that your workers should have all the authority they need but not more than is necessary to do the job in question. Inconsistencies between delegated authority, responsibility, and assigned task will produce undesirable results. You may have experienced organizations where some of the managers had a large amount of authority delegated to them but had no particular jobs to perform. They created nothing but disturbance. Then again, you may have been in positions where responsibility was exacted from you without having had the authority. This, too, is a most frustrating position. Make certain that the three components necessary to a successful process of delegation are of equal magnitude and that whenever you change one the other two must be changed simultaneously.

EXERCISE AND DELEGATION OF AUTHORITY IN PRACTICE
As discussed in the foregoing, the key to the creation of an organization is delegation of authority. If no authority has been delegated one can hardly speak of an organization. As a matter of fact, in such an instance you have often heard it said that this is a one-man organization, and you have probably seen the consequences when this one man became incapacitated, died, or for some other reason left the scene. Since in reality there had been no organiza-

tion, the enterprise literally collapsed. Hence, from an organizational point of view the problem of delegation of authority is not a question of whether or not authority will be delegated, it is a question of how much authority will be delegated to the various subordinates on the different organizational levels. It is not a question of *whether or not*, it is a question of the degree of delegation.

The extent to which authority is delegated will determine the degree to which the enterprise is decentralized. The variations of the degree of decentralization of authority are innumerable. They can run all the way from the highly centralized organization where one can hardly speak of an organization, to the organization where authority has been delegated to the lowest level of management conceivable. In the first instance the chief executive is in close touch with all operations, makes all decisions, and gives all instructions. He has delegated hardly any authority and, strictly speaking, it cannot be said that he has created an organization. There are many small enterprises which are run along these lines. It is understandable at times that the chief executive has no desire to or is in no position to delegate any authority, especially at the inception of the undertaking.

There are many enterprises where authority has been delegated to a limited degree. In those enterprises the major policies and programs are decided by the top manager of the enterprise and the application of these plans to day-to-day operations and day-to-day planning are delegated down the line to the first level of supervision, but not more authority. This kind of arrangement is often found in medium-sized enterprises. It obviously is advantageous in that it limits the number of managers which the general manager must hire, and hence he can keep the expenses down. Furthermore, it is advantageous in that the unusual knowledge and good judgment which the general manager possesses can be applied directly. There are probably hundreds of thousands of enterprises in the United States which have this type of organization with a limited degree of delegation of authority.

At the other end of the spectrum of the degree of delegation of authority we will find those organizations where authority has been delegated to the broadest possible extent to the lowest level of management. In order to find out how decentralized an organization is, it is wise to check the extent to which authority has been decentralized. In order to check this it is necessary to determine the kind of authority which has been delegated, how far down in the organization it has been delegated, and how consistent the delegations are. The criterion for delegation is an answer to the question of how significant a decision can be made by a manager, and how far down within the managerial hierarchy. The answer to this question will indicate whether or not you are dealing with an organization which has authority delegated to the greatest extent or not.

Although centralization of authority or limited decentralization is the most logical form to use in the early stages of an enterprise, the top administrator will sooner or later be faced with the problem of delegating authority and decentralizing it. Decentralization of authority becomes necessary when centralized management finds itself so burdened with decision-making that the top executives do not find enough time to adequately perform their planning function or to maintain a long-range point of view. This is one situation which would indicate to top management where authority was centralized that the time had arrived to delegate authority to lower echelons. As time goes on there will be a gradual development toward decentralization of authority commensurate with the growth of the enterprise.

ADVANTAGES AND DISADVANTAGES OF DELEGATION By delegating authority the senior manager is relieved of time-consuming detail work. Subordinates can make decisions without waiting for approval of their decisions from their supervisor. This increases flexibility and permits more prompt action. In addition to this, such delegation of decision-making may actually produce better decisions, since the man on the job usually knows more about the factors involved than the manager at headquarters and since speedy decisions may often be essential. Delegation to the lower levels increases morale and interest, and enthusiasm for the work. It also provides a good training ground. All of these advantages become even more important as the enterprise grows in size.

SUMMARY   In this chapter we have discussed the meaning of authority as that power which makes the managerial job a reality. One way of looking at the source of authority is that all managerial authority emanates from the top of the organization. From there it is delegated through an uninterrupted chain of command from the top administrator down to the supervisor on the lowest level of supervision. In this process the managerial authority is conferred upon him from above. However, this approach to the source of authority has been deeply shaken by what is commonly known as the acceptance theory of authority. This theory postulates that the supervisor only has authority if and when the subordinate confers it upon him by accepting it. According to this theory, the superior manager does not possess authority until and unless this acceptance by his employee takes place. In reality, the choice between accepting his boss's authority or not accepting it, is the choice between quitting the job and staying. Nevertheless, this kind of thinking raises serious doubts about whether or not a manager should depend on the formal weight of authority to motivate his workers. As a matter of fact, this would be the least desirable way and the least effective one.

Through the process of delegation of authority management creates the organization. The process of delegation of authority is made up of three components, namely, the assignment of a job or duty, the granting of authority, and the creation of responsibility. All three are coexistent and a change in one will of necessity cause a change in the other two. Since the delegation of authority is the only way to create an organization, the question is not whether top management will delegate authority, it is only a question of how much or how little authority will be delegated. If much authority is delegated to the lowest rank of supervision, then one speaks of a highly decentralized organization; if all authority is more or less hoarded at the top, one refers to such an organization as a highly centralized enterprise. One of the advantages arising from a broad delegation of authority is the high motivation of subordinates.

6

THE SUPERVISOR AND DELEGATION

All supervisors of a department will not have a chance to practice broad delegation of formal authority. If you have many employees within your department, it is very likely that you will create separate divisions and groups within your department over which you will put someone in charge. If your department is large enough to divide it further into subgroups, then in order to create an organization within your own department you must delegate authority to these various group leaders. They, in turn, may carry this delegation of authority further, depending on the size and magnitude of their own activity.

As a supervisor, it is very likely that you have expressed the wish to delegate authority to some of your subordinates, but you had no one within your department who was willing to accept this authority and to take charge of an area of activities. Of course, delegation of authority assumes that there is someone available who is willing to accept the authority delegated to him. In reality, you may not have anyone working for you to whom you could delegate a reasonable degree of authority, because he is simply not capable of handling it. In such a case, of course, authority must be withheld and you cannot delegate it. On the other hand, you may find yourself in a vicious circle, complaining that without trained subordinates you cannot delegate, but without delegated authority your subordinates will have no opportunity to ever obtain the necessary training. With additional experience and training their judgment could be improved, and they would become more capable subordinates. This very lack of trained subordinates is often used by supervisors as an excuse for not decentralizing. The supervisor must always bear in mind that unless he makes a beginning he will never have a capable subordinate working for him. In the early stages the degree of authority you will delegate upon him will be very small; but as he grows in his capacities increasingly more authority can be delegated to him.

It is understandable that the supervisor is reluctant to delegate authority as he knows that he cannot delegate his responsibility. He knows that in the final analysis responsibility remains with him, and he therefore thinks it is best to make all decisions on his level. Thus, out of fear of mistakes many supervisors are not willing to delegate much authority, and in so doing they continue to overburden themselves. Their indecision and their delay may often be costlier than the mistakes they hoped to avoid by retaining their authority. Always bear in mind that there is also a likelihood that the supervisor himself may make mistakes. In addition to this, it will help considerably in the training of your subordinates if they are permitted to learn from some of their own mistakes.

DELEGATION AND THE DAILY WORK   The question arises as to how a supervisor can effectively reap the benefits of delegation of authority if he has only a limited number of employees working for him and where there is no necessity to create separate groups and departments within his own division. This is probably the kind of problem which faces most supervisors. What can they do in the daily working situation to delegate authority to their employees at work?

THE SUPERVISOR'S HESITANCY   The supervisor's relutance in delegating authority is understandable in view of the fact that he still remains accountable for the results. In this respect he is right. The old picture of a good supervisor was the one who rolled up his sleeves and worked alongside his employees, thus setting an example by his efforts. Such a situation is often true of a supervisor who has come up through the ranks and for whom the supervisory position is a reward for hard work and technical competence. He has been placed in a managerial position without having been equipped to be a manager, and he is faced with new problems with which he cannot cope. He therefore retreats to a pattern in which he feels secure and works right alongside his employees. There are occasions when such participation is needed, for instance, when the job to be performed is of a particularly difficult nature or if an emergency has arisen. Under these conditions the good supervisor will always be right on the job to help. But aside from these emergencies and unusual situations, he should be carrying out his supervisory job and his men should be doing theirs. It is his job not to do, but to get things done.

Frequently a supervisor has said to himself that if he wants something done right he has to do it himself. Often he also feels that it is easier for him to do the job than to correct his subordinate's mistake. And the supervisor may feel a strong temptation to correct his employee's mistakes himself rather than to explain to him what should have been done. It is frequently more difficult to teach than to do it oneself. The supervisor often feels that he can do the job better than any of his employees and the chances are that he can. But sooner or later he will have to get used to the idea that someone else can do the job almost as well as he can. The fact that someone else has done it almost as well and almost as adequately, saved the supervisor time for more important jobs, for thinking, planning, and more delegating. The supervisor will see that the employee, with every additional job, becomes more competent in what he is doing. After some time the employee's completed job is as good as the one which the supervisor may have done.

The supervisor should see to it that his employees make their own decisions. This does not mean that he will not be available for some additional advice and judgment, but he should make certain that the decisions should stem from them. Then, as time goes on, the supervisor will develop some confidence in his employees, and he can devote his time to the more important job of managing. As the supervisor sees his employees perform increasingly more jobs almost as well as he can, as they recommend solutions which are almost as good as the supervisor's, the supervisor's belief and confidence in his workers will grow. This, of course, is a long, tedious process and the degree of delegation will vary with each subordinate and with each working situation. But basically the underlying policy must be that of delegating more and more authority to the employees in your department.

In spite of the fact that authority must be delegated if there is to be an organization, there are some supervisory duties which cannot be delegated. It should always remain to the supervisor to form policies and give the general directions for his department or division, to take necessary disciplinary action, to promote an employee, and to appraise immediate subordinates. But aside from these and other specific duties, his employees should do everything themselves.

THE EMPLOYEE'S GENERAL ATTITUDE AND REACTION   Most of your employees accept work as a part of a healthy, normal life. In their daily jobs they seek a satisfaction which wages alone cannot provide. Most employees enjoy being their own bosses. They like a degree of freedom to make their own decisions pertaining to their work. The question arises of whether this is possible if one works for someone else, and, can such a degree of freedom be granted to him if he is to contribute his share toward the achievement of the enterprise's objectives. This is where the delegation of authority can help. This desire for freedom, being one's own boss, can be enhanced by the delegation of authority which in a working situation merely means giving orders in broad, general terms. It means that the supervisor, instead of watching every detail of the employee's activities, is primarily interested in the results the worker achieves and permits his subordinates to decide how to achieve these results.

The delegation of authority in the daily working situation does not amount to more than a general form of supervision whereby the supervisor sets the goals and tells his subordinates what he wants accomplished, fixing the limits within which the work has to be done. But he lets his employees decide how to achieve these goals. In other words, he gives each employee maximum freedom —naturally, within the constraints of the organization. This broad, general kind of supervision on the employee level has the same results as the delegation of formal authority in the higher levels of management.

There are significant advantages to this approach of supervision, the same kind of advantages which have been cited in our discussion of the process of delegation of authority. The supervisor who learns the art of delegation will benefit in many ways.

If the supervisor exercises his supervision in general, broad terms he will first of all have more time to handle his own job as a supervisor. The supervisor who believes in close and detailed supervision and who tries to make every decision by himself exhausts himself physically and mentally. With delegation he will be freed from the many details of his work in order to have time to plan and to control. In so doing, he will, in turn, have more time to receive and handle more authority which his boss will then delegate to him.

In addition to the foregoing advantages, there is no certainty that the supervisor's detailed decisions may be as good as those of his employees since the man on the job is closest to the problem. Furthermore, this general, broad supervision gives your employee a chance to develop his talents and abilities. It is always very difficult to instruct your employees to make decisions without putting them into a position where they have to make them. They can learn only by practice. Of course, you as a supervisor have to state the limits and tell your workers what is expected of them. Many supervisors are afraid to let the employees make their own decisions as to how the job is to be done because they are afraid of mistakes which may ultimately injure the supervisor's position. It is not advocated that a supervisor sit idly by to let employees make mistakes which would hurt the institution; but, on the other hand, there is also no guarantee that if he specifies the details of the job mistakes will not take place. Only by giving your employees the practice to decide and to use their own judgment can they become more independent and better workers.

The third advantage of this general type of supervision is that it will give your employees a chance to take great pride in the results of having made their own decisions on the job. As stated before, employees take great pride in being on their own. Repeatedly surveys have shown that the one quality which employees most admire in a supervisor is his ability to delegate. Employees want a boss who shows them how to do a job and then trusts them enough to let them do it on their own. Furthermore, in so doing you provide on-the-job training for them and a chance for better positions. This kind of general supervision is a sure way for progress for the supervisor himself, for his employees, his department, and the enterprise as a whole. Much more will be said about this general supervision when we discuss the managerial function of directing and supervising. Let us therefore repeat at this time that on the worker's level the delegation of authority often does not amount to more than a general, broad kind of supervision instead of an autocratic, dictatorial, detailed method. But, by pursuing this broad, general kind of supervision many of the satisfactions which your employees seek on the job and which money alone does not cover, are fulfilled, so that they are motivated to put forth their best efforts in achieving the enterprise's objectives. This is what this kind of delegation of authority to the workers will bring forth.

DELEGATION AS BUILDER OF MORALE, WITHOUT DEPENDENCE ON AUTHORITY In any organization one of the supervisor's most important and prevailing problems is how to motivate his employees so that they willingly and enthusiastically perform their function toward the organization's overall objectives. There was a time when management believed that emphasis on authority was the best way of motivation in industry. Those who depended on the force of authority as means of motivation—and a few may still erroneously believe in this today—thought that this method consists of forcing people to work by threatening to fire them if they did not. One of their assumptions was that the only reason people work is to earn money and that they will work only if there exists the fear of losing their jobs. This approach ignores the fact that employees want many other intrinsic on-the-job satisfactions from the work besides the salary. This approach also assumes that people do not like work, that employees try to get away with doing as little as possible. Therefore, there is need for very close supervision. They believe that the supervisor must tell the workers precisely what is to be done every minute of the day and not permit the worker any chance to use his own judgment.

Such reliance on the sheer weight of authority, of course, has lost most of its followers. This kind of approach was possible in the early days of the industrial revolution when workers were close to starvation, where they would do anything in order to obtain food, clothing, and shelter. In recent years, however, employees have begun to expect much more from their jobs and, therefore, the "be strong" policy has become less effective. First of all, employees are not only looking for economic satisfactions on a job, but other satisfactions also. This is particularly so when times are good and employment is high. In addition to this, the educational process of our children has had a significant influence on the more recent attitudes. Many years ago children were used to strict obedience to their elders. But now schools and home emphasize freedom and self-expression, and therefore it is becoming more and more difficult for the young employee to accept any kind of autocratic management on the job. In addition to this, the growth of unions has made it difficult for a supervisor to fire an employee.

Those who believe in the sheer weight of authority and the "be strong" form of motivation have also ignored the fact that workers will react in ways which were not intended by their supervisor. This sheer weight on authority provides no incentive to work harder than the minimum which is required in order to avoid punishment and discharge. They will produce only the minimum which is necessary to keep them from getting fired. Under those conditions, also, the employees will fight back, which, if they are not unionized, will materialize in slowdowns, sabotage, and spoilage. To this management will likely react by watching these workers even closer. This, in turn, will encourage the employees to try to outsmart management. Thus a vicious circle is started with new restraints and new methods of evading them. Furthermore, the reliance on the sheer weight of authority will cause innumerable other difficulties, so that instead of finding satisfaction in their daily work employees will become frustrated. Sooner or later this frustration may show itself in aggression, arguments, fights, and a general devastating effect on the entire organization.

Of course, delegation is delicate. It is not easy for a supervisor to part with some of his authority, still to be left with full responsibility for decisions made by his workers. Therefore, good delegation requires sound judgment and skill. The supervisor must weigh between too much or too little delegation and the happy medium must be achieved in order to delegate enough without losing control.

SUMMARY   On the supervisory level the proper delegation of authority expresses itself primarily in the practice of a general supervision by giving the employee a great amount of freedom in making his own decisions and in the manner of doing his own job. This will enable the employee to use his own judgment, and in so doing he will receive satisfaction from the job in which he is engaged. This form of general supervision is probably the best way to motivate the employees of the supervisor's department, whereas dependence on the sheer weight of authority would normally bring about the least desirable results. There are occasions when the manager must fall back on his authority. But this will be the exception rather than the rule.

PART II

PLANNING

7

THE MANAGERIAL PLANNING FUNCTION

Planning is one of the five functions of the manager. Planning is deciding in advance what is to be done. Logically, planning must come first. When the manager plans he projects a course of action for the future, attempting to achieve a consistent and coordinated structure of operations aimed at desired results. Of course, plans alone do not bring about the desired results; in order to achieve them the operation of the enterprise is necessary. But it is likely that without plans only random activities will prevail, producing confusion and possibly even chaos. Planning is a managerial function which the manager must use consistently every day. It is not a process used by a manager only at occasional intervals when he is not too engrossed in his daily chores. By planning, the supervisor realistically anticipates future problems, analyzes them, anticipates the probable effect of the various forces on the activities of the enterprise, and decides on the plan of action which will lead to the desired results.

Planning is mental work, and for many managers difficult to perform. But there is no substitute for the hard thinking which planning demands. It is necessary to think before acting and to act in the light of facts rather than of guesses. Planning is a primary function which must come before the manager can intelligently perform any of the other managerial functions. Only after having made his plans can he organize, staff, direct, and control. How could a supervisor properly and effectively organize the workings of his department without having a plan in mind? How could he effectively staff and supervise his employees without knowing which avenue to follow and without knowing what the goal is? And how could he possibly control the activities of his employees? He could not perform any of these functions without having planned first. When planning, the manager decides in advance which of the alternative courses are to be followed, which policies, procedures, methods, and so on will be set up.

EACH MANAGER PLANS   The question often has been raised as to who does the planning. It is the manager who must do the planning, and it is the job of every manager whether he is chairman of the board, the administrator of a hospital, or the supervisor of a department. By definition all of them are managers, and therefore all of them must do the planning. However, the importance and the magnitude of the plans will depend on the level on which they are performed. Naturally, management's planning on the top level is more fundamental and more far-reaching. As we descend toward the supervisory levels of management, the scope and extent of planning becomes narrower and more detailed. The administrator is concerned with the overall aspects of planning, whereas the supervisor is concerned with the plans for getting the job in the department done promptly and effectively each and every day.

Although planning is the manager's function, it does not mean that he may not call on others to help him. The supervisor may feel that certain areas of his planning call for special knowledge, such as those areas dealing with personnel policies, accounting procedures, or technical aspects. In such instances he must feel free to call on specialists within the organization to help him with his planning responsibilities. In other words, the manager should avail himself of all possible help he can get within the organization to effectively do his planning. But in the final analysis it is his responsibility to plan.

IMPORTANCE OF PLANNING   Planning is important not only because it makes for a purposeful organization, but it is also important because it minimizes costs. By deciding in advance what is to be done, how and by whom, where it is to be done, and when, it makes for purposeful and orderly activities. All efforts are directed toward a desired result, haphazard approaches are minimized, activities are coordinated, and duplications are avoided. Minimum time is necessary for the completion of all planned activities because only the necessary work is done. Facilities are used to their best advantage and guesswork is eliminated. As a supervisor you are entrusted with the management of a group of employees and with the administration of physical resources. You have to work with factors such as space, tools and equipment, materials, and so on. Only by planning will the supervisor be able to make the best possible use of these resources entrusted to him. Only by planning will the supervisor be able to bring out the best in his employees. Plans for the best utilization of the resources entrusted to the supervisor are essential, among other reasons, because of the capital investment that the hospital has made for the most effective functioning of his department. Considerable investment is made to provide him with the necessary working space, tools, equipment, materials, and supplies. Even in the smallest department the total investment is a substantial sum. Only by planning can all of these resources be utilized most efficiently.

PLANNING PERIOD   For how long a period ahead should the manager plan? Usually a distinction is made between long-range and short-range planning. The definition of long-range and short-range planning depends on the manager's level in the organizational hierarchy, on the type of enterprise, and the kind of industry in which the undertaking is engaged. For all practical purposes short-run planning can be defined as planning which covers a period up to one year. Long-term planning usually

74

involves a time interval of three to five years or even more. It is likely that the supervisor's planning period will fall within the short-range planning period, namely, planning for one year at the most, six months, one month, one week, or perhaps even just for one day. There are activities in some departments for which the supervisor can plan for three, six, nine or twelve months' activities in advance; for instance, in the planning of preventive maintenance by the engineering department. On the other hand, there are other activites in a hospital and related health facilities where most supervisory planning will be for a week, for a day, or only for a shift. Such short-range planning is frequently employed, for instance, in the nursing services. Of course, it is more desirable if the supervisor is in a position to make longer-range plans than planning for very brief periods, but for all practical purposes the supervisor must give most of his attention to seeing to it that the work of each day gets accomplished. Such short-range planning for the day is always necessary. It means that the supervisor must take time out to think through the nature and the amount of work that is to be done by his department. This planning must be done ahead of time, and many supervisors like to do this at the end of one day when they can size up what has been accomplished in order to formulate the plans for the following day. This probably is the least amount of planning which every supervisor has to do.

There are occasions when a supervisor will have to pay some attention to longer time spans in his planning. When the need arises, his boss may discuss with the supervisor the part he is to play in the planning of the broader future objectives of the institution. The supervisor may be informed of a contemplated expansion or the addition of new facilities, and he will be asked to make an estimate of what his department can contribute, what he will need in order to achieve the new objective, and questions of that type. From time to time the supervisor might also be asked by the administrator to project the long-run trend of his particular activity, especially if it seems apparent that such activity will be affected by increasing mechanization and automation. Much time and effort is needed on the supervisor's part to make these long-range plans, and even more time will be needed to carry them out once they are made and approved.

Such long-range plans may indicate to the supervisor that he has to reassign or retrain part of his employees. Long-range plans may indicate that new employees with new skills need to be employed and a search made for them. This type of planning may indicate that new procedures and new techniques are necessary due to new equipment which will be introduced. Therefore, from time to time there will be need for every supervisor to participate in long-range planning. But generally this will not be the rule and his primary planning period will be that of a shorter duration. But whatever planning is going to be done, the supervisor must make certain that he is doing it ahead of time.

INTEGRATION AND COMMUNICATION OF PLANS It is necessary that the short-range plans made by the supervisor are integrated and coordinated with any kind of long-range planning the top administration may have. Therefore, it is necessary for the administrator to keep all supervisors well informed as to the existing long-range plans and objectives of the institution, and to make certain that the short-range plans of the supervisor are in accordance with them. The better informed the supervisor is, the better will he be able to integrate his short-range plans into the overall plans of the enterprise. All too often there is a gap between the knowledge of top management and second level management as far as planning is concerned. This is often explained by the claim that many of the plans are confidential and for security reasons cannot be divulged. Of course, practitioners know that very little can be kept secret in any organization. Plans should be communicated and fully explained to the subordinate managers so that they are in a better position to formulate their own derivative plans for their departments. By the same token each supervisor should bear in mind that his employees will be affected by all plans which he makes. Since the work of the employees is necessary in the execution of whatever the supervisor has planned to do, he will do well to take them into his confidence and to explain to them in advance what is being planned for the department. The employees may even be in a position to make contributions, and their ideas may be very helpful. The supervisor should always bear in mind that a well-informed employee is a better employee for the department.

VARIETY OF PLANS

SETTING THE OBJECTIVES   The first step in planning is a statement of the objectives to be achieved by the enterprise with which every member of the organization should be familiar. The objectives are the goals, the end result toward which all plans and activities are directed. They constitute the purpose of the enterprise, and without the objectives no intelligent planning can take place. The formulation of objectives is foremost among the manager's responsibilities. To set the overall objectives is a function of top management. Top administration must clearly define the primary purpose for which the undertaking is organized. These objectives may be stated in a number of ways. For a hospital, overall objectives will be care for the sick and injured, contribute to the research and advancement of medical knowledge, help in the prevention of sickness, educate and train in all professional and nonprofessional activities customarily connected with a hospital. The main objective of a home for the aged would be the total care of elderly people in a home-like atmosphere.

PRIMARY AND SECONDARY OBJECTIVES   These goals mentioned for an institution as a whole are often called the primary objectives in order to distinguish them from the goals set up for each of the various departments. Each department must have it own objectives clearly set forth as a guide for its functioning. Goals of the various departments of an organization are often called secondary objectives. Each department or division has a specific task to perform, and it therefore follows that each division must have its own clearly defined goals. Of course, the goals and objectives of the department stay within the overall framework of the primary objectives of the total organization; they contribute to the achievement of the overall objectives. Since they are concerned only with one department, they are of necessity made in greater detail. But their basic aim and contribution are, of course, within the framework of the overall objectives of the institution.

Since effective management is always management by objectives, these objectives should be stated as clearly and simply as possible. Such statements will clarify and point out the target which the supervisor and his employees are to reach. All efforts within the department must be coordinated in that direction. As head of the department the supervisor must make certain that he knows what is expected of him and of his work force if his division is to measure up to expectations. Both primary and secondary objectives should be clearly defined and stated, and thoroughly understood by every employee of the department. The supervisor must bear in mind that the successful completion of a task depends on the full undertsanding of its purpose by those who have to carry the task through. It is therefore good management to make certain that all employees at all levels are thoroughly informed and indoctrinated about the objectives to be achieved.

Whereas the overall objectives, as stated above, are broad and general, the objectives of a department will be much more specific and detailed but still fall within the framework of the overall objectives of the institution. For instance, the objective of a medical records department may read: to provide a central file of medical records compiled during the treatment of a patient that will be used as a permanent record in case of future illness; as an aid in clinical and statistical research, as an administrative tool for planning and evaluating the hospital program, and as a potential legal protection for the patient, hospital, and physician. Obviously, these departmental objectives are much narrower, but their fulfillment contributes significantly to the achievement of the overall goals. As a matter of fact, the overall primary hospital objectives could not be achieved if the subsidiary departmental objectives are not fulfilled. This clearly points out the importance and significance for all supervisors and their employees to clearly understand the objectives of their departmental unit.

POLICIES   Once the objectives of the enterprise have been determined, the manager can set about to make all of the plans which are necessary to achieve this goal. There are a number of plans which the manager must devise in order to reach the goal: namely policies, procedures, methods, rules, budgets, and so on. All of these plans must be designed to reinforce one another, and they all must be directed toward the same objectives. The major

78

plans are formulated by the top administrator, and each department supervisor will formulate his departmental plans in accordance therewith. Among the various plans often referred to, policies are probably those which are mentioned most frequently. Policies are broad guides to thinking. They are general statements which guide or channel the thinking of all personnel charged with decision-making. Although these guides are broad they do have their definite limitations at either end and thus delimit the area. So long as a subordinate stays within these broad areas he will make an appropriate decision. Policies are not narrow; if they were, they would not be broad guides to thinking. They channel the thinking of the decision-maker, and as long as he remains within the boundaries he knows he will make a decision in conformance with the policy. Policies are channels for thinking for the subordinate managers, and as such they facilitate the job of the managers and the subordinates.

Policies are a guide for the thinking of all managers to be used in their decision-making. After having set the policies, it is much easier to delegate authority, knowing that whatever decisions the subordinate makes, he will be guided by these boundaries. He probably will come up with about the same decision the superior manager would have made himself. Hence, the existence of policies makes it easier for the superior to delegate authority to his subordinate managers. On the other hand, having policies is of great help to the subordinate manager also. For instance, if the supervisor knows what the guides for his thinking are—what the policies are—this will facilitate his decision-making, and at the same time insure uniformity of decisions throughout the entire enterprise. Therefore, the clearer these guides for thinking are, and the more comprehensive they are, the easier and better will it be for the superior manager to delegate authority. A policy is a broad guide for thinking, yet it permits the supervisor to use his own judgment in making a decision which falls within the limitations of the policy.

Origin of policies Obviously, policies do not come about by chance. They are determined by the manager, and most policies are originated by top management. To formulate policies is one of the important functions of top management. The top manager is in the best position to see the need for the various overall policies which are required to guide the thinking of the subordinate managers, so that the enterprise's objectives can be achieved. Once the broad policies have been established by the top administrator, they in turn will become the guides for the various policies covering the smaller areas of departmental activities. Departmental policies are then originated by the various managers lower down in the managerial hierarchy. Of course, all of these departmental policies will implement and coincide with the broader policies of the enterprise as originated by top management.

There are occasions where the supervisor may find himself in a situation for which no policies either exist or are applicable. In such a dilemma the supervisor has only one resort, and that is to go to his boss and simply to ask him whether or not any of the existing policies are applicable. If there are none then the supervisor will ask his boss to issue a policy to cover such situations. It may happen that the supervisor has to appeal to his boss for the issuance of a policy. For instance, one of your employees asks you for a leave of absence. In order to make the appropriate decision, you would like to be guided by a broad policy so that whatever decision you arrive at would be in accord with all other decisions regarding leaves of absence. However, you may find that the administrator never issued any policies which should guide your thinking in the granting or denial of a leave of absence. Instead of making decisions for each case, you need a general guide. In such a case you must appeal to your own boss and ask him to issue a policy, a broad guide for thinking to be applied when leaves of absence are requested. It is not likely that many such instances will happen since a good administrator usually foresees the many areas where policies are needed. But it is conceivable that such an appeal to your own boss has to be made occasionally.

In addition to those policies which are handed down by top administration, there are a number of policies which are imposed upon an organization by external factors such as the government, trade unions, trade associations, accrediting associations, and so on. The word "imposed" indicates compliance with a force which cannot be avoided. For instance, in order to be accredited, hospitals and other health facilities must comply with certain regulations issued by the accrediting agency. Any policy imposed in such a manner upon the enterprise is what is known as an externally imposed policy, one with which everyone in the institution has to comply.

Clarity of policy statements Since policies are such a vital guide for decision-making, offering a broad guide for thinking, it is essential that the policies be explicitly stated and communicated so that those in the organization who are to apply them will fully understand. This is no easy task. It is difficult to find words which will be understood by all people in the same way since different meanings can be attached to the same word. Although there is no guarantee that even the written word will be properly understood, it seems desirable that the policies be given in a written statement. However, not many enterprises have written policies since many of them simply never get around to writing them down. Others purposely do not write them down.

It is not an easy task to state policies in black and white, but the benefits derived are well worth the time and effort spent in doing so. The mere process of writing these policies will require the top administrator to think out these policies clearly and consistently ahead of time. The subordinate manager can read them as often as he cares to. The meaning of a written policy cannot be changed by word of mouth because if there is any doubt the written policy can always be referred to. Furthermore, the written policy is there for anyone to read if he wants to, and subordinate managers who are new in the organization can speedily acquaint themselves. Although the advantages far outweigh the disadvantages, there are some disadvantages connected with written policies, and, realistically speaking, there are not too many enterprises which have their policies written out. Many enterprises prefer to have their policies handed down by word of mouth because they feel that this is more flexible, allowing the policies to be adjusted to different circumstances with more ease than written policies. But, this might mean that the exact interpretation is not known, and the probability of not being definite makes verbally handed down policies not too desirable.

THE SUPERVISOR AND POLICIES   There will not be too many occasions where the supervisor will have to issue policies. It is

81

conceivable that if the number of employees in the department is very large and if several subdivisions exist within the department, the supervisor may find the need for issuing and writing down policies. But whatever the departmental policy is, it is necessary that it be a broad guide to thinking and that it stay within the overall policies as set up by the administrator. Instead of making policies the supervisor will be called upon primarily to apply existing policies in making his decisions. Most of the time it is the supervisor's job to interpret and explain the meaning of policies. He will be guided by them in the many daily decisions he has to make in his contacts with the employees of his department. The supervisor seldom will have to issue policies, but he must continuously observe all existing policies as a guide in his decision-making. Therefore, it is essential that he correctly understands the policies, and learns how to apply them appropriately.

PROCEDURES Procedures, like policies, are also plans for achieving the objectives. But procedures are much more specific. Although the manager rarely will find an occasion to issue a policy, there will be many occasions for him to issue procedures. Procedures are a guide to action, not a guide to thinking. Procedures show the sequence of definite acts. They define a chronological sequence of acts which are to be performed. Procedures specify a route which will take the subordinates between the guideposts of the policies and lead them to the final objectives. Procedures pick a path toward the objective. They make for consistency by defining which steps are to be taken and in which sequence they are to be followed. Since the supervisor is the manager of his department he is the one to determine how the work is to be done. If he were fortunate enough to have only highly skilled employees under his direction, he could depend upon them to a great extent to select an efficient path of procedure. But this is very unlikely, and the employees look to the supervisor for instructions on how to proceed. It is therefore obvious that effective procedures designed by the supervisor of the department will result in definite advantages.

One of the advantages lies in the fact that the mere process of preparing a procedure necessitates analysis and study of the work to be done. Once a procedure is established it assures uniformity of performance. In addition to these benefits, procedures give the supervisor a standard in appraising work done by his employees. Inasmuch as the procedure specifies the chronological sequence of how the work is to be done, it decreases the need for further decision-making. Although the supervisor will not have much occasion to issue policies he will spend a good deal of his time and effort in devising procedures to be applied throughout his department. The same applies to the supervisor's concern with the design of methods.

METHODS A method is also a plan for action, but a plan which is even more detailed than a procedure. Whereas a procedure shows a series of steps to be taken, a method is concerned only with the single operation, with one particular step. The method tells exactly how this particular step is to be performed. For most of the work which is done by the employees of the supervisor's department there exists a "best method," a best way for the job to be done. If the supervisor were to rely on highly skilled workmen they would know the best method without having to be told. But in many instances it is necessary for the supervisor to devise what he considers the best method for getting the job done under the circumstances. A large amount of time is spent in devising methods. Once a method has been designed it carries with it all the advantages of a procedure, as cited above. In devising the best method there may be need for the supervisor to call on the help of a methods engineer or a motion and time study man, if such a person is available in the organization. In many instances, however, the supervisor's experience is probably broad enough to design the "best" work method himself.

STANDARD PROCEDURES AND PRACTICES In some divisions of the hospital there will be no need for the supervisor to be overly concerned with the devising of procedures and methods because his employees will already have been thoroughly trained in standard practices and procedures. For instance, nurses, technicians, and medical specialists are exposed to many years of schooling and training during which great emphasis is placed on the proper procedures and proper methods of performing a certain task. In the supervision of a department where such highly skilled employees are at work the supervisor's task is greatly simplified, and one of his main concerns will be to see to it that good, generally approved procedures and methods are carried out in a professionally accepted way. However, in addition to these highly trained professional specialists, the supervisor will have employees in his department who are not highly trained, for whom procedures and methods must definitely be established by him.

RULES   A rule is different from a policy, a procedure or a method. A rule is also a plan, a plan which has been devised in order to bring about the attainment of the enterprise's objectives. It is not a policy because it does not provide a guide to thinking, and it does not leave any discretion to the party involved. It is related to a procedure insofar as it is a guide to action and states what must or what may not be done. However, it is not a procedure because there is no time sequence to a particular action. No smoking, for instance, is a rule which was made by the manager, one rule of the long list of safety rules. It is just no smoking wherever and whenever it is in effect. It is a guide to action, in this instance to inaction. But it is not a procedure because there is no time sequence involved. There will be many occasions when the supervisor has to set up his own rules or see to it that the rules set up by the administration are obeyed.

REPEAT-USE OR SINGLE-USE PLANS   The different kinds of plans mentioned above—policies, procedures, methods, and rules —are commonly known as repeat-use or standing plans because they are plans which are followed each time a given situation is encountered. Repeat-use plans are used again and again. They are applicable any time whenever a situation presents itself where such a standing plan must be invoked. The opposite of repeat-use plans are those plans which are used up once the objective is accomplished. They are known as single-use plans. Once the goal is reached the plan is used up. Within this single-use plan we find programs, projects, and budgets. Since programs and projects are mainly the concern of the top administrator it will suffice in this discussion to merely clarify what budgets are.

BUDGETS   Budgets are usually thought of only in connection with controlling; but this is incorrect. Budgets are also plans, but plans which express the anticipated results in numerical terms, be this in dollars and cents, man hours, kilowatt hours, or units to be produced. A budget may be stated in time, material, money or other units which are necessary to perform work to obtain specific results. It is a statement of expected results, and that is why it is often thought of in connection with control. Of course, budgets are used in connection with controlling, but the preparing and making of a budget is planning, and this is the duty of every manager.

Since a budget is a plan expressed in numerical terms, it has the distinct advantage that the goal is expressed in exact and specific terms instead of in generalities. There is considerable difference between the making of general forecasts and attaching numerical values to specific plans. The figures which the supervisor will put into the budget are the actual plans which will become the standards to be achieved. These plans are not mere projections, but will be considered as a basis for daily operations. They will be looked upon as standards to be lived up to. It is essential that in the preparation of a budget those supervisors who will have to function under a budget will have a part in its preparation. It is only natural that people resent arbitrary orders, and it is necessary that all budget objectives and allowances are determined with the full cooperation of those who are responsible for executing the plans. These various supervisors should actively participate in the budget-making, and it should not be what is commonly known as pseudo-participation. In order to assure true participation in the budget-making process it is necessary that the subordinate manager (the supervisor) submit his own budget, that he participate in what is commonly known as grass roots budgeting. The supervisor, of course, will have to substantiate his budget proposals in a discussion with his boss and possibly with the top administrator where the final budgets will be set and adjusted. This is what is meant by active, real participation in budget-making, thus insuring its effectiveness. This should not be construed to mean

85

that the suggestion of the supervisor should or will always prevail. The supervisor's budget should not be accepted by his boss if he feels that the supervisor's plans are not adequate or correct. No plan, no budget should be accepted without a careful study and analysis by the superior manager with whom the final decision rests. Differences between budget estimates should be carefully discussed.

There are all kinds of budgets which the supervisor could plan. He can draw up a budget in which he plans the man-hours to be used for certain jobs within his department, a budget for certain materials and supplies, or the better known budget for the departmental expenditures. The latter is probably the one budget with which most supervisors are familiar. If this budget is arrived at with participation on the supervisor's part then the likelihood that he will live up to it is better than if the budget had been handed down to him by his boss.

The budget is an example of a single-use plan. It will only serve as a guideline for the period for which it is drawn up, and when this particular period is over this plan—this budget—will not be called upon again. It has served its usefulness and is no longer valid. This is why a budget is called a single-use plan.

SUMMARY   Planning is the managerial function which determines in advance what is to be done in the future. It is the function of every manager ranging from the top administrator to the supervisor of each department. Planning is important since it assures the best utilization of the resources and economy of performance. The planning period on the supervisory level is usually of a much shorter duration than it would be on the top administrator's level. Nevertheless, even the short-range plans of the supervisor must coincide with the long-range plans of the enterprise. Setting the objective is the first step in planning. Although the overall objectives are determined by top administration there are many secondary objectives which must be clarified by the supervisor and which must be in accordance with the primary objectives of the overall undertaking. In order to reach the objectives, different kinds of plans must be devised. Policies are guides to thinking, and most of them originate with the administrator. In most instances the supervisor's concern with policies is primarily one of interpreting them, applying them, and staying within them whenever he makes decisions for his department. There may be occasions when the supervisor has to appeal to his boss for the issuance or clarification of certain policies. The supervisor will often be called upon to design procedures and methods. These are guides for action, not guides for thinking. The supervisor also will participate in the establishing of budgets, which are plans expressed in numerical terms.

8

PLANNING ON THE SUPERVISORY LEVEL

Planning is deciding in advance what is to be done in the future. Although the future is fraught with uncertainties, the manager must make certain assumptions about it in order to plan. These assumptions are based on forecasts of what the future will hold, and appraisal of future prospects is inherent in all planning. In fact, the success of an enterprise depends in a large measure upon the skill of management in foreseeing and preparing for future conditions. All managers must make some assumptions of the future. Of course, the administrator must make an effort to forecast the future in a much more far-reaching manner than it is necessary for a supervisor to do. But since both are managers, both must make assumptions for the future. In his endeavor to predict the overall outlook of things to come, the administrator will be greatly concerned with the general economic climate in which the enterprise will operate during the next few years. He should be concerned with government expenditures and government spending policies. The administrator will have to make assumptions concerning the many possible future laws which ultimately would affect the activities of hospitals and related health facilities. The administrator is concerned with the outlook of monetary policy and the overall economic activities within the country. He will be vitally concerned with forecasts of changes in our population and with the aging pattern of the population. Conditions in all of these areas will affect the operations of a health care facility and since the administrator's job is of a much broader nature than that of a supervisor, the areas in which he has to make forecasts of the future are therefore more numerous and far-reaching. Although it is essential for the supervisor to make certain assumptions as to what the future will hold, especially in reference to those areas which will affect his particular activities, every supervisor will ultimately also be affected by the major trends which affect the institution in general.

DEPARTMENTAL FORECASTS   A supervisor must try to forecast the significance of his particular departmental functions. It is conceivable that there might be a growing trend for simplification of the function which he oversees, or that the particular function seems to be disappearing. He must keep a keen eye on the developments in the area of technology and automation, with an awareness of the very latest. Based on what has happened, he should venture some kind of assumption as to what the future will hold in this respect. To a great extent he can look for assistance to the suppliers of the equipment which he uses. He can learn much by attending meetings, exhibitions, and so on. It could very likely be that technology is progressing so rapidly that in a number of years a department's functions may be significantly different from what they had been. Such a projection of the future is essential in order to plan properly. The supervisor will also have to make a forecast in relation to the kind of employees who will be working for him. He may foresee the need for employees who are better educated and more skilled. He may have to look for people who possess skills which up to now have never been required or known in his department, or even anywhere in the hospital. Or it may very well be that due to increase in mechanization, less and less people will be necessary to perform the functions currently performed. Only by making an assumption as to the future will the supervisor be able to clarify in his own mind in which direction his department will go. If he sees the need for special skills with which he himself has not been familiar he should start getting busy and familiarize himself with these particular aspects, making certain where appropriate technical assistance can come from. In making these assumptions and in trying to forecast what the future will hold, the supervisor will be ready with a definite plan if and when these particular events should occur.

The supervisor must also make assumptions relating to the pattern of wages, fringe benefits, and costs in general. It may very well be that the wage pattern which is followed now can-

89

not be maintained in the future, and he would do well to start planning accordingly at an early time. In looking into the future it could conceivably appear imminent that the department which he is supervising will lose its importance altogether. It is conceivable that due to new discoveries or new means of doing the work an entire department may become obsolete. Although this is not a very pleasant thought, if this is looming on the horizon it is better for the supervisor to realize it early instead of being confronted with such an event without having been prepared for it. If obsolescence is threatened, the far-sighted supervisor will inform the administrator accordingly. Sooner or later the administrator should make it his business to carve out a new supervisory position for the particular supervisor who has been so far-sighted. He is too valuable an employee to lose and probably he can be just as good in the supervision of another department, perhaps of a department which heretofore has never existed. It is possible that in the future some activities will show up within the areas of the institution which have never been performed by it.

It should always be remembered that at the base of all forecasts lie certain assumptions, approximations, and average conditions. It must be emphasized that forecasting is an art and not a science and as yet there is no infallible way of predicting the future. However, forecasting accuracy increases with experience. As time goes on, making assumptions of the future will become a normal activity of all managers within the hospital from the administrator down to the supervisor. They will exchange ideas and help each other and supply information whenever available. Therefore, in all likelihood they in turn will work as a check on each other and the final analysis of what the future holds will probably be quite reliable. But even if many of the events which have been anticipated do not materialize or do not materialize exactly as anticipated, it is better to have foreseen them than to be suddenly confronted with them. Having foreseen these events, the supervisor is in a position to ready his mind and his state of affairs so as to incorporate changes whenever need be. Although this may sound like a formidable task for a supervisor, all that is required of him is to be alert to all possible changes and trends. It is not uncommon for a supervisor to go back over the years of his work and with the help of hindsight point out the time when certain trends were already visible, and to wish he had taken them seriously at that time. This is what the supervisor is asked to do from now on: to look into the future so that whenever those events occur which he has anticipated he is ready for the changes which are necessary.

POLITICAL CONSIDERATIONS IN PLANNING   While planing, the supervisor must keep in mind the impact of his plan on others, because the success or failure of planning will depend largely upon the reaction of those whom it concerns, be they employees, supervisors of other departments, or the boss. There are a number of tactics or political considerations at the supervisor's disposal to minimize negative reactions and facilitate the success of the plan. There are a number of possible strategies a supervisor might adopt. He must choose the one or a combination of several best suited for the problem on hand.

Since timing is a critical and essential factor in all planning, the manager may choose the strategy which tells him to *strike while the iron is hot.* This strategy obviously advocates prompt action when the situation and time for action are propitious. Then again, he may want to invoke the old saying that *time is a great healer.* This is not an endorsement for procrastinating, but often it is advisable to create an opportunity for cooling off because many things take care of themselves after a short while.

When significant changes are involved in his planning, the supervisor may do well to put to work the strategy of what is known as *mass concentrated offensive.* This strategy more or less advocates a quick radical change in order to take fast action, and to make a quick, favorable showing. On the other hand, the supervisor may prefer to just *get a foot in the door.* This tactic advocates that it may be better to propose merely a portion of the plan in the beginning, especially if the program is of such magnitude that its total acceptance would be doubtful.

Sometimes the plan may advocate changes which could come about easier if supervisors of other departments would join in the action. It therefore may be advisable to seek allies in order to promote the change. *There is strength in unity.* For instance, if the supervisor plans to increase the salaries of his employees it may be expedient to try to get the other supervisors to join with him in a general request for higher remuneration when presenting this to the administrator. Of course, this may involve another strategy which is so well known in politics: *You scratch my back and I will scratch yours.* This tactic of reciprocity is not only well known in political circles or in the activity of purchasing agents, but also among colleagues in order to present joint action on a particular issue.

There are many other strategies which can frequently be invoked and can be of help in initiating and carrying out plans. The mentioning of these tactics should not be construed to mean that they are always recommended. The list cited is most certainly not complete. The choice and the application of these political tactics will depend upon the people involved, the situation, the urgency of the objective, the external situation, the timing, the means available, and a number of other factors. Properly applied, they can minimize difficulties and increase the effectiveness of the manager's planning.

PLANNING FOR THE UTILIZATION OF RESOURCES

As stated in the beginning of this chapter, the supervisor has been entrusted with a large number of resources so that he can accomplish the job of his department. It is his duty to plan specifically how to utilize the resources available to him, so that the work of his unit is accomplished.

PLAN UTILIZATION OF TOOLS AND EQUIPMENT   The supervisor must plan the full utilization of the tools and equipment provided for his department. This frequently represents a substantial investment the institution made for him. By proper planning he will get full use out of this investment. It is the supervisor's job to appraise the tools and equipment in his unit, to ascertain whether or not there are better machines available for doing the work. It is his job to observe the employees using the equipment and question them whether they serve the purpose well. It is not necessary for a supervisor to always have the very latest model of each tool available; but, on the other hand, he should plan to get rid of inefficient tools and equipment if he can replace them with better ones. Of course, there is still the question to be settled of when this change should take place. It is the supervisor's job to look at trade journals, to listen to what salesmen of tools and equipment have to show him about their products, to read the literature which is circulated by hospital and related associations, and to keep himself aware of the general development within his field. It is the supervisor's job to submit his plans for replacement of tools and equipment to the administrator. He should recommend the changes with all the possible reasons he can think of, but he will have to leave the final decision to those above him. Even if the request should be turned down the supervisor has demonstrated that he is on the job and planning for the future. He will also find that in the long run his plans for replacement of equipment and additional new equipment will be accepted. And even if his request should be curtailed the administrator will have to admit that as a manager he planned for the utilization of the equipment for his department.

PLAN WORK METHODS AND PROCESSES The supervisor must make plans concerning improved work methods and processes in his department. The difficulty is that many supervisors work under considerable pressure and find little time for this type of planning. Nevertheless, in order to maintain high efficiency in your department it is necessary from time to time to study the operations performed in order to plan improvements in the work methods. The supervisor is often so close to the jobs to be performed that he believes that the prevailing work methods are satisfactory and that not much can be done about them. The supervisor would do well to look at his operations as a stranger coming into his department for the first time, to look at his operations with a detached point of view and observe all methods and processes. He should ask himself if an operation is really necessary, what the reason for it is, whether or not it could be combined with something else. Are the various steps performed in the best possible sequence, are there any avoidable delays, and so on? In his efforts to plan better work methods it is possible that the supervisor can call on the help of a staff specialist, such as a methods engineer, who may be available within the hospital. Approaching this problem of work methods with a detached point of view it is very likely that better methods and processes can be planned for the future.

PLAN USE OF SPACE   By the same token, it is necessary for the supervisor to plan for the best utilization of space. He will have to determine whether or not the space assigned to his department is used effectively. In his efforts to devise the best utilization of the space allocated he again may call on some industrial engineering help if this is available. In order to plan effectively, he should make a layout chart for himself and this picture then can be studied to determine whether he has the appropriate area in which the work is to be performed and if the space allocated has been laid out appropriately. These plans could possibly envision the need for additional space. If such a request is placed before the administrator with thorough planning of the space allocated, the likelihood that such a request will be granted is better than otherwise. The supervisor must realize that he has to compete with many other supervisors who probably also request more space, and if his planning has been done thoroughly his request has a better chance of being granted. Even if the request is denied, the plans drawn up have not been in vain. In all probability they will have alerted the supervisor to some of the conditions under which his employees are working. This, in itself, may have some beneficial consequences.

PLAN USE OF MATERIALS AND SUPPLIES   The supervisor must plan for the appropriate use and conservation of materials and supplies entrusted to the operation of his department. In most departments the quantity of materials and supplies used is substantial. Even if each single item represents only something of small value, the aggregate of these items adds up to sizeable amounts in the budget of a hospital or related health facility. Proper planning will insure that materials and supplies will be used as conservatively as possible, thus bringing about good performance within the department. The supervisor must plan for proper use because many of the employees do not realize the significance of the amount of money involved, or even are careless in this respect. By proper planning the supervisor can call the workers' attention to this and explain to them that the economic use of the supplies is to their own advantage, pointing out that whatever is wasted cannot be used to raise their wages or to improve working conditions. Although proper planning for the utilization of materials and supplies will help significantly in performance, it will not prevent all waste.

PLAN THE USE OF TIME   The supervisor must also plan the use of time. The old saying "time is money" applies with equal force to the supervisor's own time and to his employees' time. Not only must the supervisor plan good use of his employees' time, he must also consider at least as carefully the use of his own time.

The supervisor's time The supervisor's own time is one of the resources for which he must plan carefully. It is likely that every supervisor has experienced days which were so full of pressures and demands that he began to feel as though he could never take care of all the matters that needed attention. The days and the weeks just were too short. The only way to keep such days to a minimum is for the supervisor to plan his time for the most effective use. Unfortunately, the supervisor's problems come up on a continuous line but without any sequence of importance. He first must sort and grade them, he must decide between those matters which he must attend to personally and those which he can delegate to someone else. There are some matters which the supervisor actually cannot delegate; but there are many matters which in reality can be delegated to his employees. Every time the supervisor dispenses with one of his duties by assigning it to one of his employees he is gaining time for more important matters. This is worthwhile even if he has to spend some valuable time training one of his employees in a particular task. In case of doubt he should be inclined to delegate. Then he should plan his available time so that it is divided among those matters to which he alone can attend. He will again have to classify them according to those which are most urgent and those which are not.

Unless the supervisor distinguishes between those matters which must be done and those which ought to be done he is inclined to pay equal attention to all matters before him, and the more important ones may not get the attention they truly deserve.

But by distinguishing he will be giving those more priority which need them and should have more attention. He should therefore plan his time so that the most important things he has to attend to will have been given sufficient space on his schedule. The supervisor must make certain that he leaves some flexibility in his own time schedule because not every contingency that will occur can be anticipated. There will be emergencies to which he must turn his attention when they arise. The flexibility will permit him to take care of these situations without significantly disrupting his own time schedule.

Many techniques have been devised to help supervisors control their time schedules. One of the simplest methods is to do this with the help of a desk calendar, scheduling those things which need attention, appointments, meetings, reports, discussions, etc. The supervisor should schedule events far in advance and in so doing they will automatically come up for his attention when they are due.

Another effective way of planning each week's work in advance and of knowing what is being accomplished as the week goes on, is to keep a planning sheet. Such a planning sheet is prepared at the end of one week for the week to follow. It shows the days of the week divided into morning and afternoon columns and a list of all things to be accomplished. Then a time for accomplishment is assigned to each day by blocking out the morning or the afternoon blocks of the assigned day. Thus at a glance the supervisor knows what is planned for each morning and afternoon of the week. As each task is accomplished the box is circled. Those tasks that have been delayed must be rescheduled for another time by blocking out the time on a subsequent day. Those tasks which are planned but have not been accomplished during the week (they are still uncircled) must be rescheduled for the following week. Such a record will show how much of the original plan has been carried out at the end of the week and it provides a good answer to the question of where the supervisor's time went. Based on this record he will then be able to plan his next week, and so on. Regardless of which particular system the supervisor uses, he must make it his duty to plan his time for his work for each week and to have some method of reporting the tasks that are planned and those which have been accomplished.

The employees' time In planning the effective use of the time of his employees the supervisor expects that his employees will turn in a fair day's work. The supervisor cannot expect his employees to work indefinitely at top speed; his plan for their time should be based on a fair output instead of a maximum output. Allowances must be made for fatigue, unavoidable delays, and in general, a certain factor of unproductive time during the work day. In planning the employees' time the supervisor may be able to call on the help of a staff specialist employed by the hospital, preferably a motion and time specialist. Normally, most supervisors have a pretty fair idea as to what can be expected of the employees timewise. Such reasonable estimates of the employees' time are necessary, because their work must be scheduled in order to complete the various operations on time, and the supervisor must depend on the completion at a certain time. The supervisor in turn may have been given deadlines, and in order to meet them he must have a fairly good estimate or idea of how fast the job can be done. Most supervisors are capable of planning reasonable performance requirements of their employees which they accept as fair. Such estimates are based on average conditions and not on emergencies.

In planning the effective use of the time of the employees the supervisor largely depends on studies concerning work methods and processes. Also, the introduction of new and better equipment and tools may alter the time schedules so far valid. All of this will bring about a better utilization of employee time. Some jobs carry their own deadline whereas others do not. In many instances it is advisable for the supervisor to set a completion date as a deadline is always helpful in bringing about the completion of a project sooner than if none had been set.

In addition to planning the normal employee time, there may occasionally be the necessity to plan for overtime. In planning the employees' time, overtime should be considered only as an emergency matter. If the supervisor finds that overtime is reguuarly required then he should change his plans by alternate methods or by hiring more employees. The supervisor must also plan for employee absences. Of course, he cannot plan for those instances when employees are absent without notice. But the supervisor can plan for holidays, vacations, layoffs for overhaul, and occasions of that type. Plans for this kind of absence which

97

can be anticipated must be made in advance, in order to assure the smooth functioning of the department. If possible, they should be worked out as far in advance as feasible so that the functioning of the department will suffer as little as possible.

PLAN UTILIZATION OF WORK FORCE   Although a supervisor must plan for the utilization of tools and equipment, for improved work methods and processes, for utilization of space, for conservation of materials and supplies, and for the proper use of his time and his employees' time, the most important planning of all is that connected with the utilization of his work force. After all, the employees he has available in his department are his most important resource. To plan for the full utilization of his employees must be uppermost in the manager's mind. This does not mean planning to receive as much work as possible from an employee. Utilization means giving the employees as much satisfaction as possible in their jobs. To plan for the best utilization of employees means to make plans for recruiting the employees, to search for all possible sources of employees. To plan for best utilization of the work force means to search continuously for ways to best group their activities. It includes the problems and plans of training and supervising them. The plans include the broad area of motivation. The question of appropriate utilization of the workers means the continuous appraisal of their performance, appropriate promotions, adequate plans of compensation and rewards, and at the same time, if need be, fair disciplinary measures. All of these considerations play an important role when the supervisor plans for the best utilization of his employees. Only by planning for the best utilization of his employees will the supervisor create a situation wherein his workers willingly contribute their best in order to achieve personal satisfaction on the job, at the same time contributing their utmost toward the achievement of the department's objectives. The supervisor may rest assured that whatever efforts he makes in this connection will be rewarded amply by his employees. Actually, this matter of planning for the best utilization of his employees is the core of expert managing. It is discussed here only briefly, but most chapters of this text are concerned with bringing about the best utilization of employees.

SUMMARY   All of this planning for the future must be done with a forecast of the future in mind. Since the future is uncertain, it is necessary to make certain assumptions as to what the future may bring. The overall forecasts are made by the top administrator, and the supervisor narrows these down to forecasts for his particular activity. It is up to him to correlate the assumptions with the activities of his department. Based on these assumptions the supervisor in turn will make the plans for his own department. In so doing he should be concerned with the effect his planning may have on other members of the organization. Therefore, at times he may resort to political considerations which may be helpful in effectively carrying out these plans and in getting them accepted. To be specific, the supervisor must plan for the full utilization of the resources he has at his disposal in his unit. He must plan for proper utilization of tools and equipment, of work methods and processes; he must make plans to utilize the space made available to him and the materials and supplies under his supervision; and he must effectively plan the use of his time and the time of his employees. But primarily, he must plan for the best possible utilization of the employees in his unit.

PART III

ORGANIZING

9

SPAN OF SUPERVISION, DEPARTMENTS, LINE AND STAFF

In performing the organizing function the manager groups and assigns activities of his area so that they can be most effectively executed. At the same time he establishes the authority relationships between these various activities and departments. While performing his organizing function the manager is concerned with the building, developing, and maintenance of a structure of working relationships that will bring about the objectives of the enterprise. In order to make such a structure possible the manager delegates authority throughout the organization and establishes the authority relationships between the various departments. It is the objective of organizing to group activities in a fashion that will coordinate the efforts within these departments toward the common objectives of the undertaking, and so that the objectives can be achieved with the greatest economy and effectiveness. The process of organizing takes place at all managerial levels, and it is one of the five functions of every manager. Although organizations may have a variety of objectives and may operate in many kinds of environments the application of the basic concepts and principles of organization is universal.

The administrator as an organizer groups the various activities of a hospital or a related health facility into distinct departments and assigns the various duties to be performed to these divisions and departments. At the same time the administrator puts a supervisor in charge of each of these departments. Furthermore, the administrator establishes the authority relationships, so that the supervisor of each department knows precisely who his boss is and who his subordinates are. While arranging authority relationships in this fashion the administrator follows the principle of unity of command. Unity of command means that there is one person in each organizational unit who has the authority to make the decisions appropriate to his position. It means that each employee has a single immediate supervisor who is in turn responsible to his immediate supervisor, and so on up and down the chain of command.

To organize the overall aspects of the entire institution's activities is the job of the administrator. However, it is every supervisor's job to organize the department over which he has been put in charge, and it is therefore necessary that he become familiar with what it means to organize. No doubt the range and the problems of the supervisor's organization will be of a much smaller dimension than those of the administrator. But the principles to be called upon in organizing are the very same.

SPAN OF SUPERVISION

The establishment of departments and the creation of the various managerial levels are not an end in themselves. They are not desirable per se because departments are expensive; they must be headed by various supervisors and their additional staffs, all of which runs into large sums of money. Furthermore, they are undesirable per se because the more departments and levels which are created the more difficulties will be encountered in communication and coordination. Therefore, there must be a good reason for setting up departments. The criterion lies in what is commonly known as the principle of the span of management or the span of supervision. This principle states that a manager can effectively supervise only a certain number of subordinates and not more. Often this principle is known as span of managerial responsibility, span of management, span of authority, or span of control. It is preferable to use the term span of management or span of supervision as these two are most meaningful.

Almost every supervisor knows that there is a limit to the number of employees he can effectively supervise. Since no one can manage an infinite number of subordinates, there is the necessity for a manager to create departments, distinct areas of activities over which he places a manager in charge. To this manager he delegates authority and he in turn may redelegate authority to some of his lower subordinates, who in turn, will supervise only some of these employees. If a manager could conceivably supervise one hundred employees effectively all of these one hundred subordinates could directly report to him and their various activities would not have to be grouped into departments. But, obviously, this is impossible.

The fact that a manager can effectively supervise only a limited number of subordinates is as old as mankind. It is not possible to state a definite figure as to how many subordinates a manager could have reporting to him. It is correct to say only that there is an upper limit to this number. Although no definite figure can be determined, it is interesting to note that in practice we find that in many industrial concerns the top administrator has anywhere from five to eight subordinate managers reporting to him. As we descend within the managerial hierarchy we will find that the span of supervision increases. It is not unusual to find anywhere from fifteen to twenty-five people on the supervisor's level. Actually, the number of subordinates who can be effectively supervised by a manager depends on the various factors which we shall discuss in the following.

FACTORS DETERMINING THE SPAN OF SUPERVISION   One of the factors which influences the magnitude of the span of supervision is the training, experience—the know-how—the supervisor has acquired. Obviously, there are some supervisors who are capable of handling more subordinates than others. Some are better acquainted with good management, have had more experience, and simply are all around better managers. If a man is a "good manager" he probably can supervise more employees. The number of subordinates a manager can supervise is limited because human capacity is limited; a manager only has a certain amount of time available during the working day, but what the manager does during that time is of utmost importance. It takes more time for the supervisor to make an individual decision for every problem that comes up, than it does if he were to take the time to make policy decisions which anticipate problems that might arise later. Clear and complete policy statements reduce the volume of, or at least simplify, the personal decision-making required of a manager, and hence increase his span of supervision. The same applies to other managerial processes that determine in advance definitions of responsibility and authority, performance standards, programs, procedures, and methods. Predeterminations such as these reduce the number of decisions the manager has to make, and hence increase his potential span of management. Therefore, one of the important factors in determining the number of employees a supervisor can effectively supervise is the quality of his supervisory ability.

Another factor on which the manager's span depends is the amount and nature of the work he must do, and particularly whether he can call for help from specialists within the organization. If the hospital has a range of experts who provide various kinds of advice and service then the manager's span can be wider. For instance, if the personnel department does a good job in servicing and assisting the supervisor in the procurement of employees, the supervisor of the department will have more time and energy available to increase the number of subordinates he can manage. But if he will have to do all the recruiting, pre-interviewing, and testing himself, then, obviously, he cannot devote that portion of his time to the management of his department. Therefore, the amount of additional help available within the institution will influence the width of the span of supervision.

Another factor which will determine how broad a span a supervisor can effectively manage will be the capacities and the makeup of the employees in the department. The greater the capacities and self-direction of the employees, the broader a span is feasible. The training possessed by the subordinates is also of importance. The better their training, the less they will need their supervisor. Hence, the more subordinates he can manage. The number of subordinates will also depend on the variety and importance of the activities performed by the employees. If the activities to be supervised are highly important and complicated activities it follows that the span of supervision will, of necessity, have to be small. But the simpler and more uniform the work, the greater can be the number of persons supervised by one supervisor. If the task to be performed is repetitious, the span may be even as broad as twenty-five to thirty employees. If the activities are varied and of great importance the span might have to be as small as three or five.

Other factors that have a bearing on the span of supervision are the dynamics and complexity of a particular activity. Some aspects of the hospital routine are most certainly of a dynamic nature whereas others are of a more stable character. In those departments which are engaged with dynamic and unpredictable activities the span will have to be narrower. In those departments which are concerned with more or less stable activities the span of supervision can be broader. Another factor which will determine the span of supervision is the degree to which objective standards are or can be applied. If there are enough objective standards available for the subordinate to check on whether or not he is on the right track, he will not need to report to and contact his boss. Good objective standards will result in less frequent relationships and therefore make for a broader span of supervision. Another factor influencing the span of management is time itself since no one can change the minutes in an hour. Time itself presents a very real limitation of the span of management because a supervisor has only so many hours during each day. He obviously cannot very well have one hundred subordinates reporting to him.

These are some of the factors which will determine the span of supervision, or in other words, the number of subordinates a supervisor can effectively supervise in each and every instance. There is no set figure which can be quoted. The principle tells us only that an upper limit exists.

LEVEL VS. SPAN If, based on these considerations, the span seems to be too broad, it is the supervisor's job to break up this broad span into two or three groups over each of which he places someone in charge. By narrowing the span to a smaller number of employees, the supervisor, of course, creates one more level of management because over each of the smaller groups a foreman or lead man has to be placed. What happens is that the narrower the span of supervision becomes, the more levels of management have to be introduced into the organizational setup. This again is not desirable per se because not only does it cost money, but it also complicates communications and control. Therefore, there is a constant conflict between the width of the span and the number of levels. The problem, therefore, is whether to have a broader span of supervision or more levels, and this is one of the important problems with which the top administrator is faced throughout his entire career. The supervisor is not too frequently confronted with this question as the number of subordinates he usually has is a small one. But the problems are the very same, namely, whether it would be more advisable to have a broader span or a narrower span with more levels of managers within the managerial pyramid. (See figure 3)

DEPARTMENTATION

By departmentation we understand the process of grouping various activities into separate units. A department is a distinct area of activities over which a manager or supervisor has been given authority. The terminology often varies, and a department may be called a division, a service, a unit, or some similar term. For all practical purposes, the major departments are set up by the administrator, and the supervisor is only concerned with the activities of his own area. Nevertheless, from time to time he too may be confronted with the need for smaller areas within his own department, and it is therefore necessary for him to be acquainted with the number of alternatives he has available for grouping activities. The patterns most commonly found in departmentation are groupings by function, product, territory, customer, process and equipment, or by time.

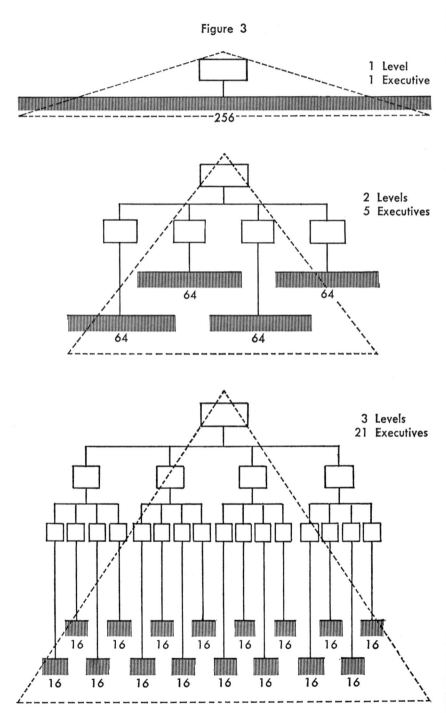

Figure 3

1 Level
1 Executive

256

2 Levels
5 Executives

64 64 64 64

3 Levels
21 Executives

16 16 16 16 16 16 16 16
16 16 16 16 16 16 16 16

BY FUNCTION The most widely accepted practice of departmentalizing is to group activities according to function—the job to be done. This is the guiding thought in the establishment of most departments within a hospital and related health facilities. All those activities which are alike and concern a particular function are put together into a department. For instance, all nursing services are normally within the nursing department. To departmentalize by function is a natural and logical way of arranging the various activities of any enterprise. To group departments along functional lines takes advantage of occupational specialization by putting together the functions which belong together, which are performed by the same specialists with the same kind of background, equipment, and facilities. Each supervisor is concerned with one type of work only, and his energy will be concentrated on it. Functional departmentation also facilitates coordination since one supervisor is in charge of all of one type of activity. It is simpler to achieve coordination this way than it would be in an organization where the same function is performed in several different divisions. Another advantage of functional departmentation is that it makes the outstanding abilities of one or a few individuals available to the enterprise as a whole. Functional departmentation is a method which has been successful over the years and it is a simple method. In short, it makes good sense.

BY PRODUCT Industry very frequently invokes the principle of product departmentation. To departmentalize on a product basis in industry means to establish each product or groups of closely related products as a product line, as a relatively independent unit within the overall framework of the enterprise. In product departmentation the emphasis is shifted from the function to the product. Product departmentation in a health care facility would probably not be appropriate if applied in the same direct sense in which industry uses it. In a more remote sense, however, the concept of product departmentation occasionally may be a useful guide to group activities even in a hospital or related institution.

BY TERRITORY Another way to departmentalize is by geograpical considerations. Again, this kind of consideration is important in industrial enterprises, but applications of it could be made even within a hospital. First of all, a hospital may be confronted with a setup where there are physically dispersed units of the institution. If the functions are to be performed in different locations—different buildings—then geographic departmentation may be feasible. The same consideration may be applicable even if all activities are performed in one building but on different floors.

BY CUSTOMER At times a manager may find it advisable to group activities based on customer considerations. This is commonly known as customer departmentation. In this case the paramount interest of the enterprise is in the peculiarities of the customers. There are many examples of organizations which have been departmentalized along customer lines: a university, where there are night programs and day programs complying with the requests and special needs of the various "customers"; a hospital where certain activities are grouped for outpatients and inpatients etc. etc.

BY PROCESS AND EQUIPMENT Activities often can be grouped according to the process involved or the equipment used. This way of grouping activities is often employed in hospitals. First of all, it takes a certain training and expertness to handle certain processes and operate equipment; everything where the use of this particular equipment is involved should be referred to a specific department. This kind of consideration may often come close to functional departmentation. For instance, in an X-ray department specific equipment is used, but also only certain functions are performed. Therefore, in this case function and equipment become closely allied.

BY TIME An additional way to departmentalize activities is to group activities according to time. An enterprise such as a hospital or a related health facility which of necessity is engaged in a continuous process must departmentalize activities on the basis of time. Everyone in such an institution is familiar with the different shifts. Activities are departmentalized by time (day, afternoon, night shift), but the activities of all the shifts are the same. Such groupings create serious organizational questions of how self-contained each shift should be and what relationship should exist between the regular day shift supervisors and the off-shift supervisors.

Departmentation is not an end in itself. In grouping the activities the supervisor should not attempt to draw a pretty picture. His prime concern should be to set up departments so as to facilitate the realization of the objectives. In so doing it is likely that the supervisor will use more than just one of the guides for departmentalizing and he may end up with a mixed departmentation, i.e. the nursing supervisor (functional) of the third floor (geographic) on the night shift (time). In practice most enterprises have a composite departmental structure invoking functional organization, geographical departmentation, and the other considerations. All of these choices are available to the supervisor; they should facilitate the grouping of activities. There are some departments as defined by the administrator where these additional departmental subgroupings are not necessary. But there are others, for instance the maintenance and engineering department, where subgroups are necessary. If the maintenance department is of any size, sooner or later it will become necessary to separate the various skills into different groups over which a lead man or foreman is in charge and who, in turn, will report to the supervisor. Thus, it is likely that the chief engineer will have under his supervision a number of departments and a number of lead men or group supervisors. The guides for departmentalizing mentioned above will be of significant help to him in setting up the various groups within his own maintenance department.

ASSIGNMENT OF ACTIVITIES

The question of where to assign certain activities will be a much more frequent problem to the supervisor than the question of how to set up departments. The objective, of course, is to assign activities so as to provide the best arrangement within the department. Naturally, the supervisor must deal with people, and as long as he has to do this there will always be differences of opinion. It is therefore best if an assignment of activities can be justified and explained on the basis of logical guides rather than on personal likes and dislikes or hunch and intuition. This is important also because the supervisor will be subject to pressures from different directions when he assigns activities. There will be those who wish to acquire more activities and there will be those who feel they should not be burdened with certain duties. And in spite of having guides available, it will often be difficult for the supervisor to make the decision of where best to place a certain activity.

One way to group activities is, of course, to assign a certain activity to those who will make use of it most of the time. Or one may be inclined to assign an activity to those employees who are particularly skilled in a certain area and primarily interested in it. If there is special interest then the likelihood is good that those employees will carry out the activity in the best manner.

One of the supervisor's important responsibilities is to assign work so that everybody gets a fair share and so that every employee can do his part satisfactorily. In order to achieve this, of course, the supervisor must clearly understand the nature and the content of the work to be accomplished. Furthermore, he must be thoroughly acquainted with the capabilities of his employees. All of this is not always easily accomplished. The supervisor is often inclined to assign heavier tasks to those employees who are more capable because that is the easiest way out. However, in the long run it would be far more advantageous to train and bring up the less capable employees so that they also can perform the more difficult jobs. If too much reliance is placed on one or a few persons the department will be in a bad spot if they are absent or should leave the employment of the enterprise. It is necessary to have a sufficient amount of employees available who have been trained. The supervisor's problems of assigning various activities will become less difficult as he builds up the strength and experience of all of his employees.

LINE AND STAFF

In hospitals and related health facilities it is common to speak of the medical staff, the nursing staff, the maintenance

110

staff, the administrative staff, etc. In this connection the word "staff" is used for a group of people who are engaged primarily in one activity to the exclusion of others. In this meaning the word "staff" is used to define all those people who do about the same thing, e. g. nurses, doctors, dieticians, and so on. However, in all the discussions and writings concerned with management and administration the meaning of the word "staff" is a very different one and within the context of this book any reference to "staff" is not the one to which people engaged in hospital and related activities are usually accustomed.

Much has been written and said about line and staff, and there probably is no other area in the field of management which has evoked as much discussion as this concept. It probably is also true that many of the difficulties and frictions encountered in the daily life of an organization are due to line and staff problems. Misconceptions and the lack of understanding of what line and staff are is probably the source of many bitter feelings and conflicts of personalities, of much disunity, duplication of effort, waste, lost motion, and so on.

DEFINITIONS As a supervisor of a department you must know whether you are attached to your organization in line authority or if you are staff. You can find this out by reading the job description and if this does not clarify it, by asking your superior manager. Line and staff are not characteristics of certain functions. Line and staff are characteristics of authority relationships. Therefore, the only way one can determine whether a department is related to the organization structure as line or as staff is to examine the intentions of the administrator. It is he who will confer line authority upon a certain department or place it into the organization structure as staff. Staff is not inferior to line authority; it is of a completely different nature. The objectives of the staff elements, of course, are ultimately the same as those of the line organization, namely, the achievement of the institution's objectives.

In every organization there is a straight, direct line of authority which can be traced from the top administration down to the lowest level of supervision. Line authority is the ultimate authority to direct others, and to require them to conform to decisions, policies, and goals. The primary purpose of line authority is to make organization work. This straight, direct line organization has a great advantage in that each subordinate knows exactly where he stands, to whom he can give orders and whose orders he has to obey. There is a directness and unity of command which can be traced in a straight, direct line from one to the other. This, of course, has great advantages and results can be achieved precisely and quickly. This kind of straight line organization was appropriate at a time when organizations were not as complex as they are today. In most enterprises activities have become so specialized and complicated that hardly an executive can be found who could properly and expertly direct all of his subordinates in all phases of the activities without some additional assistance. This need for additional help has been recognized for a long time. It has been evident that the line officer, in order to perform his managerial functions well, needs someone to lean on, someone who can give him counsel, advice, and service. In short, he needs a staff. Staff is auxiliary in nature and helps the line executive in many ways. It provides counsel, advice, and guidance; but it does not issue orders or commands except within its own staff department. It is the function of staff to provide this guidance, advice, counsel, and service to all members of the organization whenever and wherever there may be a need. Obviously, staff is not inferior to line and line is not inferior to staff. They are just different and both are needed to complement each other in order to achieve the objectives.

FUNCTIONS OF STAFF   Every supervisor must know whether he is attached to the organization as a line officer or in a staff capacity. He must know this so that he will understand his function and relation to the other members of the organization. If he is staff, then his function is to merely provide guidance, counsel, advice, and service in his specialty to whomever may ask him for it. But as far as his own department is concerned it will not matter whether he is line or staff. Within his own department the supervisor is the line manager. Within the department he is the only boss regardless of whether the department is attached to the organization in a staff or in a line capacity.

112

It is common practice that within a hospital certain activities are undertaken as staff. But this does not mean that one can assume that these activities are always staff. Line and staff are, as stated before, characteristics of authority relationships and not of functions. Nor does the title offer any clue in recognizing line or staff. In industrial enterprises it is common to find a vice-president of engineering, a vice-president of industrial relations, a vice-president of production. The title does not indicate whether he is in a line or staff capacity. In most hospitals and related health facilities it is likely, for example, that the personnel manager and his department are in a staff capacity. The function of the personnel department is to provide advice and service concerning matters of personnel to all departments of the hospital. The personnel department is there to recruit, screen, and test applicants, to keep the personnel records, to help in providing for reasonable wage and salary administration, to advise the line managers when difficult problems of discipline arise, and so on. Whenever the line manager has a personnel problem the personnel department is there for him to call on. The personnel manager is the one who is best qualified to supply the best current advice and information since this is his background and only duty. But all he can do is to submit suggestions to the line manager, who in turn can accept, alter, or reject them. If the line supervisor should feel that the suggestions of the personnel department are not feasible, he is at liberty to make his own decision. In all probability, since the staff people are the experts on a particular question, their advice will be accepted. After all, they are the ones who really ought to know best. So, for all practical purposes, the "authority" of the staff lies in their thorough knowledge and expertise of dealing with the problems in their specialty. They will sell their ideas based on their authority of knowledge, but they cannot "tell."[1]

---

[1]It is unfortunate that in some hospitals such a clear demarcation does not exist; there are even enterprises where staff is given the authority to decide on certain questions, and one then speaks of functional staff authority. Mention of this is made here only in order to cover the subject fully.

The staff man has the task of furnishing counsel, advice, and service in a specialized field in which he has specialized knowledge and skills which the line officer badly needs. Fulfilling these tasks is his responsibility. If any of the suggestions of staff are to be carried out they are carried out as orders and under the name and responsibility of the line officer and not that of the staff man.

Proper identification and thorough understanding of who is line and who is staff is of great importance to the proper functioning of an organization. A person who acts in a staff relationship must know that his task is to advise, counsel, and guide, and not to give orders except within his own department. He should understand that the orders must be issued by the line officer, following the regular chain of command. At the same time, the line executive must realize that the staff merely supplies advice and counsel, and that it is not a command. He is under no obligation to accept the advice and counsel of the staff. He may accept it, alter it, or completely reject and disregard it. For all practical purposes, of course, the line executive probably will heed the staff's advice. This is the reason for his hiring him, and if he no longer has need for or has lost confidence in the expertness of the staff, then he should either abolish the position or replace the staff man with someone else.

Some of the practical aspects of line and staff interrelationships will be discussed in Chapter 12 in connection with the discussion of the supervisor's staffing function and the activities of the personnel director. This discussion will illustrate the difficulties often encountered in line-staff relationships, for example, how the interactions between a personnel manager (assuming he is staff) and a line supervisor can cause many problems. The importance of knowing and understanding the difference between line and staff and the misunderstandings which confused demarcations can bring about will be emphasized further.

SUMMARY The manager's organizing function is to group and assign activities, and design a structural framework to achieve the institution's objectives. To organize also means to establish the authority relationships between the various managers and departments. This is every supervisor's job within his own department. The organization structure follows the principle of unity of command, which means that each member of the organization has a single immediate supervisor who in turn is responsible to his immediate supervisor and so on up and down the chain of command. In assigning the number of employees reporting to one supervisor, the principle of span of supervision must be observed. The principle holds that there is an upper limit to the number of employees a supervisor can effectively manage. The actual width of the span of supervision is determined by a number of factors such as the capability of the supervisor, the previous training and experience of the subordinates, the amount and nature of the work to be performed, and the dynamics of the activities of the particular department. No definite number can be quoted as the ideal number of subordinates to be supervised by one manager, and the above factors must be taken into consideration in each situation. Whenever the span of supervision is decreased, meaning that the number of employees to be supervised is reduced, an additional manager has to be introduced for the excess employees. In other words, the smaller the span of supervision, the more levels of supervisory personnel are needed. This will shape the organization either into a tall, narrow pyramid or in the case of a broad span of supervision, into a shallow, broad pyramid. The manager is aided by several guidelines in his endeavor to group activities into specific departments. The most widely used concept of departmentation is grouping activities according to functions, and placing all those who perform the same activities into the same department. Besides departmentation by functions, it is possible to departmentalize along geographic lines, or by product, by customer (patients), by process and equipment, or by time (shifts). More frequently than setting up departments within his own division, the supervisor will be faced with the question of assigning activities. Of course they should be assigned in such fashion as to provide an optimum arrangement. In this endeavor the supervisor will be guided by such principles as assigning activities to those who will make most use of them, who have the best experience in doing this kind of work, who are particularly trained, and so forth. In addition to these considerations, the supervisor must assign activities in such fashion that all his employees have a fair share of the task to be accomplished.

Each supervisor of a department is attached to the organization either in a line or a staff capacity. Since these two authority relationships are quite different, it is essential for each supervisor to know in which of the two he finds himself within the organization. Staff is not inferior to line or vice versa. Line and staff are not characteristics of a particular function; they are characteristics of authority relationships. In order to find out in which one of the two a supervisor finds himself, he must consult his job description, organization manual, or get the answer directly from the administrator. If the supervisor finds himself in the straight, direct line of command which can be traced all the way up from his position to the top administrator, he is within the line of command. If he does not find himself within this chain of command he is attached to the organization as a staff to provide counsel, service, and advice to whomever in the organization needs it. Within his own department every supervisor is a line manager regardless of whether he is running a line department or a staff department. If he is in a staff capacity, his function is to furnish counsel, guidance, advice, and service in a specialized field. The line manager has the privilege of accepting or rejecting staff's advice and counsel. Every large organization has a number of employees whose superior knowledge and skills are employed to aid others to do a better job. The specialists who do the aiding are normally referred to as staff people. The relationship between staff and line has been known to cause frictions; but there is no reason why they should not learn to work together harmoniously.

10

DECENTRALIZATION OF AUTHORITY AND ADDITIONAL ORGANIZING FACTORS

DELEGATION OF AUTHORITY

As stated before, the key to any organizational structure is the delegation of authority. If no authority has been delegated, one can hardly speak of an organization. Hence, from the organizational point of view the problem of delegation is not a question of whether or not authority has been or will be delegated, it is a problem of how much authority is delegated to the various subordinate managers on the different organizational levels. The extent to which authority is delegated will determine the degree to which the enterprise is decentralized. The components of the process of delegation of authority have been discussed previously in connection with authority and responsibility.

In order for delegations of authority to be effective, a sincere desire and willingness to delegate authority must permeate the entire organization. Top administration must not only preach but must also practice delegation of authority. Although top management's intentions may be the best, it is conceivable that at times the desired degree of decentralization of authority is not achieved. For instance, when top administration finds that authority has not been delegated as far down as it was intended to be, somewhere along the line there may be found what is known as an authority hoarder, who simply will not delegate authority any further. He grasps all the authority which has been delegated to him without redelegating any of it.

There are a number of reasons why some managers resist decentralization of authority. To some, the delegation of authority may mean a loss of status, a loss of power and control. Others may feel that by having centralized power they are in closer contact with the administrator. And other managers are truly concerned with the expenses involved in delegating authority.

ACHIEVING DELEGATION OF AUTHORITY   There are several ways to achieve the degree of decentralization which is desired by top administration. As stated before, the entire managerial group must be indoctrinated with the philosophy of decentralization of authority. They must understand that by carefully delegating authority they do not lose status, nor do they absolve themselves of their responsibilities. One way to accomplish delegation of authority is to request that each subordinate manager have a fairly large number of subordinate managers reporting to him. By stretching his span of management, the subordinate has no choice but to delegate authority. Other enterprises have adopted the policy that they will not promote a manager until he has developed a subordinate manager who can take over his position. By doing this, they force the manager to delegate authority so that his junior managers can become efficient enough to eventually take over his job. If this is the policy, a manager should delegate as much authority as he possibly can at an early stage.

THE SUPERVISOR AND HIS BACKSTOP   Let us now turn our observations to the situation in which the supervisor finds himself as a delegator of authority. In an earlier chapter we discussed the supervisor as a delegator of authority in his daily working situation. The emphasis was on the manner in which he exercises the authority vested in him. It was advocated that in his daily contacts with his employees a general form of supervision leaving the employee on his own as much as possible would be a far better way to make use of his authority than close and autocratic exercise of this power. In the present discussion we will be concerned with the supervisor's delegation of authority as a means of building a minimal organization structure within his own department, so that when the supervisor suddenly is removed from the scene, the operations would go on with some semblance of orderliness.

We assume that the supervisor in his position of running the department, has been given sufficient authority and that he is completely in charge of all the activities within his section. Just as any other manager, the supervisor is faced with the necessity of delegating some of the authority that has been handed down to him. As mentioned previously, unless he does so he does not create any organization. He must do this if he should be in charge of very many employees. But in many instances the number of employees within a supervisor's department is reasonably small, and he may wonder if it is necessary for him to delegate authority. The likelihood is that he will need someone whom he can ask to take things over if he should have to leave either temporarily or for any length of time. Even in the smallest department there should be someone who can work as his backstop. It is not unusual that there is no one in a department who can take over when sickness hits or the supervisor has to be away from the job. It may also happen that the supervisor himself misses an important promotion because he has nobody to take over the department he would leave. So sooner or later everyone needs a backstop.

Throughout these chapters the advantages of delegation of authority and getting things done through employees have been cited. But there are some peculiar problems which the supervisor faces in the selection and training of an understudy to bring him to the point where he can delegate some authority to him. The chances are that there is no one in the department readily available as an assistant. Such a person has to be trained by the supervisor, and in this process of training it is very likely that the supervisor himself will learn some things. It will force him to get a much clearer view of his own duties, of the workings of the department, and the various jobs to be performed. Bringing an understudy to the point where he finally can be given authority will be a tedious and slow process. But it is worth the effort.

The first step in developing an assistant is, of course, to select the right person for the job. No doubt the supervisor knows who among his group of employees are the better ones, who are the ones to whom the other employees turn in case of questions, and who are looked upon by the rest of the employees as their leaders. Such a man should be an employee who knows

119

how to do the job, who seems to be able to handle his problems as they arise, who does not get into arguments, and who is highly regarded by the other workers in the department. He should have shown some good judgment in the way he organizes and goes about his own job, and in the way he solves problems as they arise. He should have an open mind, and be interested in developing himself and moving into better positions. Without his ambitions in this respect even the best training would not achieve any results. He must have shown a willingness to accept responsibility and must have proven his dependability. Sometimes a worker may not have had the opportunity to show all of this. But whatever qualities remained latent show up rather quickly during the actual training process. If the supervisor has two or three equally good employees in his department, he should start training all of them on an equal basis. Sooner or later it will be obvious which one has the superior ability. Once the selection of one is made, it is not necessary to come out with important formal announcements in this respect. Much more important than these formalities is for the supervisor to follow through by laying a thorough groundwork for good results so that the one who has been selected will become an understudy. This is by far better than announcing such a selection with much fanfare and possibly dropping the idea shortly thereafter.

Although the phrase "training a subordinate" is frequently used, the term "training" is not appropriate. It is much more of a self-development on the subordinate's part which is necessary in order for him to advance. He must show his eagerness to develop himself and have the initiative to be a self-starter. Such a development process takes a long time and cannot be accomplished in a few weeks or few months.

Since no two people are alike, no definite procedures can be outlined which will work in each and every case in the same manner. However, there are some common procedures in the training of a backstop which seem to have worked well in most situations. Gradually the boss should let the understudy in on the workings of the department. The supervisor should explain some of the reports to him and show him how he gets the information he needs. He should tell him what he does with these reports and why it is done. He should introduce him to the people with whom the supervisor deals and have him contact them as time goes on. It is advisable to take the understudy along to some of the meetings after he has had a chance to learn some aspects of the supervisor's job. At that occasion the supervisor should show him how the work of the department is related to that of the other departments of the hospital. As daily problems arise the supervisor should let the understudy participate in them and even try to solve some for himself. All of this, of course, cannot be achieved overnight. By letting the understudy come up with some solutions to problems, the supervisor will have a chance to see how well he analyzes and how much he knows about making decisions. At that time the supervisor can fall back on what he himself knows about the basic process of decision-making, and he can point out some of the steps to his understudy. As time goes on the understudy may continue to ask questions on those points which the supervisor may have neglected to explain. This would be an indication that he is a self-starter and has the ambition to make himself a valuable assistant to the supervisor.

In time the supervisor should give his understudy some areas of activities for which he will be responsible. In other words, he should give him his head, and gradually more duties and authority. All of this, of course, will take time and cannot be achieved by any miracle, or overnight. Whatever has been said throughout these chapters in relation to delegation of authority will hold true here also. This relationship requires an atmosphere of confidence and trust, and the boss must be looked upon by the understudy as a coach and friend and not as his boss. The supervisor should caution himself that in his eagerness to develop the understudy as rapidly as possible, he does not overload him or pass problems on to him which are beyond his capability. The supervisor must never lose sight of the fact that it takes time to be able to handle problems of magnitude.

Obviously, all of this will take a great number of the supervisor's hours and much effort. And it is conceivable that just about the time that the understudy comes to the point where he can be of some real help, he may be transferred to another job outside of the supervisor's department. This may be discouraging for the moment, but the supervisor may rest assured that the administrator will give him credit for the training job which he has done within his department.

THE RELUCTANT SUBORDINATE   Delegation of authority and the training of an understudy is, of course, a two-sided relationship. Although the supervisor may be ready and willing to turn over authority, there may be reasons why the subordinate is reluctant to accept it. Frequently the subordinate feels that he may not be able to tackle the job and is unsure of himself. Merely ordering him to have more self-confidence, of course, would have little effect. But the supervisor can create this self-confidence by carefully coaching and training the subordinate to undertake more and more difficult assignments. It often happens that the employee who has a great sense of responsibility is inclined to underrate himself, and in all likelihood this is the kind of employee who will probably work out to be an excellent understudy as time goes on.

Many of the reasons for a subordinate's reluctance to accept a better assignment can be dissolved by the tedious and continuous coaching of the supervisor. In order to achieve effective delegation a close personal relationship must develop between the supervisor and his immediate understudy. This will be a growing and a shifting relationship which will take on more meaning as time goes on. In due time the understudy will have developed to such a point that if need be he could take over the running of the department for the supervisor. When that happens, the supervisor has created an organization which will carry on even if he should be removed from his position. Although the foregoing is centered around the development of one assistant, the same will hold true if the size of the department should warrant a number of assistants. With the increased responsibilities there should be adequate positive incentives for the backstop, and they must be commensurate with added responsibilities. These incentives may be in the form of pay increases, a fancier title, recognized status within the organization, and other rewards of a tangible and intangible nature.

RECENTRALIZATION OF AUTHORITY   From time to time it may happen that top management will have to take a fresh look at the organization and may have to recentralize authority. Top management may feel that it has lost control over certain activities, probably because the controls established were not effective. In such a case top administration will recentralize authority. This means to revoke delegated authority and generally realign functions and duties. Such a periodic review of the degree of authority delegation is not only advisable but absolutely necessary in any organization. All of this also applies to any supervisor and the delegations he has made.

THE IDEAL ORGANIZATION

When designing the organizational structure of his department the supervisor should plan for the ideal organization in the meaning of that organization which is most desirable for the achievement of the stated objectives. It is the supervisor's job to build an organizational setup which will be best for his particular department. It is not essential that the supervisor's plans for his department look pretty on paper or that his chart look symmetrical and well balanced. It must be the ideal and most appropriate organizational arrangement to reach his particular departmental objectives. In planning the ideal organization the supervisor must consider this ideal organization as something of a standard with which he can compare his present organizational setup. It is of value to the manager to look at the ideal organization structure as a guide to the long-range plans he has for his department.

The supervisor should design his organizational setup based on sound organizational principles regardless of the people with whom he has to work. This does not mean that departments could exist without people to staff the various jobs. Without people there is no organization. However, the problems of organization should be handled in the right order—first comes the sound structure, then the people he has to work with. If the ideal organizational setup is planned first around existing personnel, then existing shortcomings will be perpetuated. Too much emphasis may be given to one activity and not enough to another position. If a department is structured around personalities it is easy to imagine what happens if the particular employee should be promoted or should resign. If, however, the departmental organization is structured on the need for personnel rather than on the incumbent personnel, it should not be difficult to find a proper successor for a particular position. Therefore, an organization should be designed which will first best serve the objectives of the department; then the various employees should be selected and fitted into these positions.

This is easier said than done. It frequently happens, particularly in smaller departments, that the available employees do not fit too well into the ideal structure. On the other hand, they cannot be overlooked. In most instances it is also true that the supervisor has been put into the managerial position in an existing department without having had the chance of deciding on the structure of his department. In these instances the best the supervisor can do for the time being is to adjust the organization to fit the capacities of the employees he has. Personal adjustments are necessary, but fewer of them will be necessary if the supervisor first makes a plan of the organization he would like to have if the ideal human material were available. Then, as time goes on, the supervisor will strive to come closer and closer to the ideal departmental setup.

ORGANIZATIONAL TOOLS

In his organizing function the manager will be considerably helped by such organizational tools as organization charts, manuals, and position descriptions. In all likelihood these are available in most hospitals and related health facilities, and it is the supervisor's duty to familiarize himself with them. In so doing he will learn the position and relations of his own department within the overall setup, and he will learn about the functioning and relationships of all other departments within the institution. It may even be necessary for the supervisor to devise some of these organizational tools himself.

ORGANIZATION CHARTS   Organization charts are a means of graphically portraying the organization structure at a given time, a task which is relatively easy to accomplish. Let us assume that no chart exists for the department over which the supervisor is in charge, and having such a chart would greatly simplify the supervisor's job. Most of the time the chart starts out with the individual job as a basic unit shown as a rectangular box. Each box represents one job. These various boxes are interconnected in such fashion as to show the grouping and activities which make up the department, division, or whatever other part of the organization is under consideration. It can readily be determined who reports to whom by merely studying the position of the blocks in their scalar relationships.

There are a number of advantages in establishing a chart of the existing department. As a graphic portrait is drawn up, the department's organization is analyzed. In preparing the chart, structural faults might show up and possibly also duplication of effort and other inconsistencies. In recording the chart, one often runs into cases where dual reporting relationships exist, where one man might be reporting to two superiors, where there are overlapping positions, and so on. The chart will quickly indicate whether or not the span of supervision is wide or narrow. An unbalanced organization is readily revealed. The chart will also help the supervisor by indicating a possible route of promotions for the employees in his department. Charts afford a simple way to acquaint the members of the department with the makeup of the division. It is only natural that most employees within the organization have a keen interest in knowing where they stand, in what relation their supervisor stands to the higher echelons, and so forth. Of course, there are some limitations to charts, especially if they are not continuously kept up to date. It is imperative that changes be recorded at once, and failure to do so makes the chart as useless as yesterday's newspaper. Although different types of charts are available, the vast majority are of the vertical type. It shows the different levels of organization in a step arrangement in the form of a pyramid.

ORGANIZATION MANUALS   The organization manual is another helpful tool for effective organization because it provides in comprehensive written form the decisions which have been made with regard to the institution's organization structure. It is a readily available reference, defining the scope of authority and responsibilities of managerial positions and the channels to be used in obtaining decisions or approvals of proposals. A manual will also be of great help in indoctrination and development of the managerial personnel. The manual should clearly specify for each supervisory manager what the responsibilities of his job are and how they are related to the other positions within the hospital. It reiterates for the individual manager the objectives of the enterprise and of his department, and it provides easy reference for explaining the complex relationships within the organization. The supervisor will do well to familiarize himself with the contents of the institution's manual, especially with those phases which affect his department.

JOB DESCRIPTIONS[1]   All manuals contain job descriptions. Job descriptions generally indicate the principal duties and functions of the various jobs, the scope and kind of authority. At times these job descriptions are short, whereas at other times they can be very lengthy. In making up job descriptions the information is obtained from the persons who hold the various positions and by a check with their supervisors. There is some confusion in the use of the term "job description" and "job specification" in practice. Generally speaking, job descriptions describe objectively the elements of a position, whereas job specifications specify the human qualities, the personal (man) specifications which are necessary to perform the job adequately. In some enterprises the job descriptions are extended to include man specifications to some degree. If the hospital should not have job descriptions the supervisor should see to it that they are drawn up. To help him in this he should be able to call on the personnel department which has the necessary experience to facilitate the job.

INFORMAL ORGANIZATION

Although many managers would like to conveniently overlook the existence of informal organization, they will readily admit that in order to fully understand the organization and how it works it is necessary to "learn the ropes," to know the informal organization. In every institution an informal structure will

---

[1]For further discussion see Chapter 12, "The Supervisor and the Personnel Department."

develop which reflects the spontaneous efforts of individuals and groups to influence the conditions of their existence. Whenever people are associated, social relationships and groupings are bound to come about. It is commonly found in organizations that several persons are in frequent contact with each other, although their relationships are not necessitated by the formal organizational arrangements. This contact may be accidental or incidental to organized activities, or it may arise from personal desire or gregariousness.

Informal organization arises from the social interaction of people as they associate with each other. At the heart of informal organization are people and their relationships, whereas the heart of formal organization is the organization structure and the delegation of authority. A manager can create and rescind a formal organization which he has designed; but he cannot rescind the informal organization since he did not establish it. As long as there are people working in the department there will be informal groups.

Informal groups satisfy the needs and desires of their members. Informal organization satisfies the members' social needs. It gives them recognition and status. Informal information through the grapevine provides a channel of communication and fulfills the members' need and desire to know what is going on. The informal organization evolves its own informal leader. Informal organization controls the behavior of others within the group and requests them to conform to certain standards set up by the informal group. Informal organization can be found on all levels from the bottom to the top and in all departments. It exists in every department regardless of the supervisor.

EFFECTS OF INFORMAL ORGANIZATION ON FORMAL ORGANIZATION The functioning of the informal organization makes the job of the supervisor a more difficult one. Because of the interdependence between informal and formal organization, the attitudes, institutions and customs of the informal organization affect the formal organization. Formal organizations, as a matter of fact, are vitalized in their conditions by the informal organizations. Informal organization can have either constructive or destructive influence on the formal organization and on the realization of departmental objectives. It is important for the supervisor to be aware of the fact that these informal groups are very strong, and that they often govern the behavior of the employees to an extent that interferes with formal supervision. Sometimes it can even go so far that the pressure of the informal group frustrates the supervisor in carrying out the policies which his superior expects him to enforce. The informal leader plays a significant role in every organization and without his cooperation the supervisor may have a hard time. The wise supervisor, therefore, should make all possible efforts to gain the cooperation and good will of the informal organization and the informal leader, and to use them wherever possible to further the departmental objectives. In practice, if properly handled by the supervisor, the informal organization can be useful to the supervisor and effective as a channel of communication and means of getting the departmental job done.

One way the supervisor can put the informal organization to the best possible use is to let his employees know that he accepts and understands the existence of informal organization. Such an understanding will enable him to group employees so that those most likely to comprise a good team will be working with each other on the same assignments. The supervisor's understanding of how informal organization works will help him avoid activities which would unnecessarily threaten or disrupt the informal organization. He should do his utmost to integrate the interests of the informal organization with those of the formal organization.

Instead of looking at the informal leader as a "ringleader" the supervisor will do better to consider him as someone "in the know" and work with him. In his effort to build good relations with the informal leader the supervisor can pass information to him before anyone else. He may ask his advice on certain problems, and put him in the "know." In so doing the supervisor must be cautious not to cause the informal leader to lose his status within the informal group because working with the supervisor means working with management. The supervisor must be careful not to extend any favors to the informal leader as this would ruin the latter's informal leadership position within the group at once. There is, of course, the additional fact that it is often difficult to identify the informal leader of a group. It is also conceivable that the group will shift from one informal leader to another informal leader, depending on the purposes to be pursued. Obviously, this is a very illusive and evasive issue. However, since the influence of the informal organization and its leader is always present and cannot be erased by the supervisor, the latter will do all in his power to get them to work with him instead of against him.

SUMMARY The delegation of authority is the lifeblood of an organization structure. Without delegation of authority one can hardly speak of an organization. Therefore, in creating an organization structure the vital factor to consider is how much authority to delegate, not the question of whether or not to delegate authority. The degree of decentralization of authority runs all the way from highly centralized to highly decentralized organizations. In reality, decentralization of authority is not easily achieved, as not all supervisors are willing to let go and delegate some of their authority to their subordinates. Unless the supervisor trains someone to be his backstop and grants authority to him, he has not created any organization and his department is bound to collapse if he has to leave the scene. From time to time the degree of delegation of authority must be reexamined, and, if necessary, recentralization may have to take place.

In designing the structural framework of an organization the supervisor should design an arrangement he would like ideally to have if he had all the appropriate employees available. Since this is seldom the case, he fits the employees at hand into this structure, thus deviating from the ideal where necessary. It would be wrong to design a structure around existing personnel.

There are a number of organizational tools which are helpful to the supervisor in his organizing job. First of all there is the organization chart which shows a graphic picture of the existing organization. In addition to charts, organization manuals will be of great help to every supervisor. They contain a statement of the objectives, the various job descriptions, man specifications, and the relations of the various positions to the rest of the organization.

Aside from the formal organization there exists in every enterprise an informal organization. Informal organization can have either constructive or destructive influence on the formal organization. In order to make the best possible use of informal organization, the supervisor must acquaint himself with the workings of the informal organization and its informal leader, and determine how he can put them to the best use in order to reach the objectives of his department.

11

COMMITTEES AND CONFERENCE LEADERSHIP

Your job as a supervisor is to get things done through and with the help of the employees of your department. If you are skilled in running and participating in a meeting, it will significantly help you in achieving this objective. Although it is a common complaint that there are too many meetings and that they take up too much time, committee meetings are a device widely used in all organizations, and there is no substitute for them. Without meetings it would be almost impossible for an organization of any size to operate efficiently and effectively. Of course, there are many different ways of supplying your subordinates with information they need to carry out a policy. There also are many different ways of receiving the ideas and opinions of your employees on how to handle a particular problem. But there is really no better way to achieve this than by holding a meeting. The real criticism of meetings is not that there are too many of them, but that the results produced often do not warrant the time and effort invested.

No doubt you have often been annoyed when you found yourself tied up in a meeting which the chairman allowed to amble along in all directions and to "cover the waterfront" without any purpose whatsoever. In the meantime work was accumulating on your desk. Very likely the chairman had not properly prepared the meeting, and his performance did not increase your respect for his managerial ability. If you look at conference leadership in this way, you can quickly see how important it is for a supervisor to acquaint himself with committee meeting and conference leadership technique. He should learn how to run them well and participate effectively. Meetings will then become increasingly interesting and stimulating because the conferees will have the satisfaction of knowing that the meeting is accomplishing something.

There has been a growing emphasis on meetings within today's corporations and enterprises, and every supervisor has occasion now and then to be involved in a meeting of some kind or another. First of all, this is due to the fact that most enterprise activities have become more and more complex, with increasing specialization. Of course, this increased specialization in turn makes coordination in these enterprises more difficult and at the same time more urgent. Conferences and meetings have proven to be a good remedy. Another reason for this emphasis on meetings is the growing realization that people are more enthusiastic about carrying out directives and plans which they themselves have helped to devise, than they are about carrying out plans that are handed down from above. The increasing importance and number of meetings makes it so much more necessary for the supervisor to familiarize himself with the workings of a committee. There are occasions when the supervisor may be the chairman of a committee and other times when he may be only a member of a committee. And then there are many occasions when the supervisor will have to act as a conference leader or chairman of a discussion group made up only of employees of his own department.

COMMITTEES

DEFINITION   A committee is a group of people to whom a matter has been committed. They meet for the purpose of discussing those matters which are assigned to the committee. The members who make up the committee normally have other duties and their committee work is merely a part-time assignment. The committee functions only as a group and as such it differs from other managerial devices.

COMMITTEE AS A PLACE TO INFORM OR TO DISCUSS   Most management meetings may be described as either informational or discussion. The informational type of meeting is the kind wherein the discussion leader does most of the talking in order to present certain information and facts. The supervisor makes an announcement and the meeting is called as a substitute for posting a notice or speaking to each employee separately. It may be expensive to take the whole work force away from the job; but, on the other hand, it guarantees that everyone who is in the department is notified of the new directive at the same time. Such a meeting also gives subordinates a chance to ask questions and to discuss the implications of the announcement. Care should be taken that questions from the participants are largely confined to further clarification of the supervisor's remarks.

In the discussion type of meeting the chairman encourages the participation of the members, in order to secure their ideas and opinions. The supervisor could ask the individuals singly for suggestions on how to solve a problem. Instead, he calls a meeting for the same purpose. It is up to the supervisor to make the final decision and to incorporate or not to incorporate some of the suggestions. Nevertheless, his employees will derive great satisfaction from knowing that their ideas have been considered and that some of them may even be used. It is likely that some good suggestions may be offered, and in all probability the implementation of the suggestions will be more enthusiastic if the various employees of the department have participated in finalizing them. The supervisor can go even further than merely asking for suggestions. He may call a meeting for the sole purpose of having the employees of his department fully discuss and handle a problem themselves, and come up with their own decision. This goes further than merely soliciting suggestions. In other words, meetings can be held for all of these purposes. Although these meetings may be of a formal or an informal nature, although they may be called for the purpose of giving information, for discussion to elicit suggestions only, or for discussion to arrive at a decision, the skills in conference leadership are the same regardless of the purpose and occasion of the meeting. These skills are important and illustrate the need for the supervisor to become acquainted with the workings of committee meetings. Again, bear in mind that these skills can be learned, and in the following this subject matter will be discussed further.

BENEFITS OF GROUP DISCUSSION   As stated above, the purpose of the committee meeting may be of a purely informational nature. The conference is called in order to make an announcement to the members of a department or a group of employees. Or a subject may be committed to a group of people for group deliberation and consideration. The purpose is to investigate and discuss the problem and to conclude these deliberations with some recommendation and suggestions to the executive. There is little doubt that a group of individuals exchanging opinions and experiences often comes up with a better solution than any one person thinking through this problem. It is an old saying that two heads are better than one. Various people will bring to a meeting a wide range of experience, background, and ability, which would not be available if the same subject had been committed to one man alone. Many problems are so complicated that a single person could not possibly have all the necessary knowledge, background, and experience to come to a wise solution. The free oral interchange of ideas will stimulate and clarify thinking. Thus the chances are that the recommendation which the group reaches is better than the one that any one member of the group would have selected if he had acted upon it alone.

Group deliberation can be a real help in promoting coordination. Members of the committee become more considerate of the problems of the other committee members. It is also likely that a suggestion which is made up from the contribution of many members of the group is likely to be carried out with greater enthusiasm than a suggestion that came from one person. It is well known that when an individual has participated in the formulation of a plan, he is more likely to be motivated in seeing that it is properly executed than if he has not been consulted. In reality it matters little how much he actually contributed to the plan, as long as he was a member of the committee and sat in on the meeting. In this respect group meetings are advantageous in promoting coordination, cooperation, and motivation.

In spite of all of these beneficial features, you are familiar with the fact that the committee device has often been abused. Often committees are created to delay action, and many people have come to think of the committee as a debating society. Jokes about the committees are numerous. It has been defined as a group that keeps minutes but wastes hours; where the unwilling appoint the unfit to do the unnecessary. Remarks are often made that there are meetings all day without leaving any time to get the work done, and so on. These disparaging references to committees are unfortunate. If the members are wisely selected, and if the meetings are efficiently directed and utilized, the committee or conference can be of remarkable help to any enterprise.

COMMITTEE AS THE DECISION-MAKER In addition to the committee whose purpose is to spread information and/or merely discuss a matter, there are those committees to which authority has been delegated to make decisions. Just as a supervisor can delegate authority to decide a problem to an individual subordinate he can call a meeting and delegate the authority to the group to handle the problem that involves the group as a whole. In these instances the committee has decision-making power: line authority. It may happen that some of the employees cannot get together on the allocation of overtime, and they ask the supervisor to decide. Naturally, he could make a decision for them, but it would be better if they could find a solution themselves. In such a case it may be best to let the decision be made by the group instead of by the supervisor. In this case management really does not care what decision is made as long as the time allotted for overtime is not exceeded. By letting the group make this decision they will come up with a solution which is accepted by the group. If such a solution is only adequate and not necessarily the best, it is better to have an adequate solution that is implemented by the group with great enthusiasm than to have a perfect decision that meets their resistance. There are many problems and many areas where management does not care what decision is made as long as it remains within certain boundaries.

COMPOSITION OF THE COMMITTEE If the subject matter to be deliberated or to be decided upon is of sufficient magnitude the committee device is a good opportunity for bringing together the representatives of several different interest groups. Specialists of different departments and activities can be brought together in such fashion that all the interested parties have proper representation. This will result in balanced group integration and group deliberation. The various representatives will feel that their interests have been heard and considered. Of course, the top administrator should see to it that this concern with proper representation will not be carried too far. It is more essential to appoint capable members to a committee than merely representative members. The ideal solution, of course, is to have a capable member from each pertinent activity on the committee. This problem of selection, of course, does not exist when the supervisor meets with his entire group of employees at a group meeting. Then, of course, all of them should be included.

Number of members No definite figure can be given as to the size of a committee necessary for effective action. The best that can be said is that the committee should be large enough to provide for thorough group deliberation and broad resources of information. However, it should not be so large that it will be unwieldy and unusually time-consuming. If the nature of the subject under consideration is such that a very large committee is needed, then it might be wise to form various subcommittees which will consider problems broken down for subcommittee consideration. Again, this problem of number does not exist if the meeting covers only the employees of a supervisor's department. In that case the number of employees in the department will establish the number of those who will participate in the meeting.

LIMITATIONS OF COMMITTEES   As stated previously, it is very likely that after having attended certain meetings, you, yourself, have considered them a complete waste of time and effort. One of the most often-voiced complaints about committees is that they are exceedingly time-consuming. This they are, since each member is entitled to have his say and often uses up a great amount of time in order to convince other members of the committee of his point of view. In addition to costliness in time, committees also cost money. It is obvious that the managers' time spent in committee meetings is not spent otherwise, and whatever their salaries are will be expended at that occasion. In addition to this, there might be travel expenses involved and additional expenses for the preparation of meetings. Another shortcoming of committees is that responsibility does not weigh as heavily on the committee's shoulders as it would on one individual who may have accepted it. Since a subject matter has been referred to the committee as a group and not to the individual members, it becomes everybody's responsibility, which in reality means it is nobody's responsibility. It is difficult to criticize the committee as a whole or any individual member since each one can hide behind the responsibility of the "committee." This thinning-out of responsibility is natural and there is no way of avoiding it if the subject has been charged to the committee. On the other hand, the many advantages emanating from group deliberation will, in all likelihood, outweigh this disadvantage.

HOW TO ACHIEVE EFFECTIVE OPERATION OF THE COMMITTEE AND EFFECTIVE CONFERENCE LEADERSHIP

It is exceedingly difficult to make committee meetings and conferences a success because the goals are so numerous and difficult to achieve. The goals of a meeting are: first, to come up with the best suggestions or best solution to the problem under consideration; second, to do this with the greatest amount of unanimity; third, to accomplish this in the shortest period of time. This is a difficult task, but not insurmountable.

A meeting should be called only for a subject worth holding a meeting about. If the topic can be handled by a telephone call there is no need to call a conference. The subject under deliberation must be clearly prescribed and understood, and the scope of the area to be covered must be delineated and clarified. Let the members of the committee know precisely what the job is. The degree of authority must be specified, which means it must be clearly stated whether this committee is to serve merely in an advisory or informational capacity, or as a decision-making body. The members should be selected appropriately, as outlined above, and their number should be reasonable. In many instances five to seven members will be sufficient. However, as previously mentioned, more important than the number of the committee members are their qualifications.

CONFERENCE LEADERSHIP   Even after the above-mentioned requirements are fulfilled the success of any meeting will depend largely on the chairman's ability to handle it. His familiarity with effective group work is necessary in order to bring the meeting to a satisfactory conclusion.

There is no doubt that the individual members of a committee bring to the meeting their individual patterns of behavior and points of view. The chairman must know how to handle the membership in such a way as to fuse the individual viewpoints and attitudes so that teamwork will develop for the benefit of the group. It will take considerable time and patience on the chairman's part to create a closely knit group out of the members so that they are in a position to integrate their various opinions and judgments. It is only human nature for committee members to think first of how a new proposition would affect themselves and their own working environment. These kinds of assumptions can easily lead to unnecessary frictions. People will see the same "facts" differently. Words mean different things to different people. The first necessity, therefore, is to find agreement on the basic nature of the problem under discussion so that everybody understands what the issue is. Therefore, it is often wise for the chairman to try to find out from the participants what they think the issues are in order to learn whether or not they understand them as they actually are.

It will take time and patience on the chairman's part before a group of individuals will settle down as a smoothly working social group. A frequent comment about committees is that the problems on the conference table are really not as difficult to deal with as the people around the table. Individuals at a meeting will react often toward each other rather than to their ideas. For instance, just because A talks too much everything he suggests may be rejected. Or, B is someone who automatically will reject whatever someone else is for. And then, there is C, that member of the committee who keeps his mouth shut all the time. It will take patience and skill on the chairman's part to overcome all of these difficulties. Then, sooner or later the members of the committee will start reacting toward the content of the meeting, the issues involved, and not the individuals around the table. For a meeting to be successful it is necessary that the various members forget about their personalities, their outside allegiance, and work together as a team which will move the meeting toward a solution of the problem to be considered. In all of this the chairman plays the most important role.

THE CHAIRMAN The role of the chairman is a most difficult one for many reasons: First, the meeting must bring about the best solution to the problem. Second, there should be the greatest amount of unanimity. Third, all this should be done in the shortest possible period of time. The accomplishment of all this will depend to a great extent on the conference skills of the chairman. No doubt the quality of the decision depends greatly on the amount of time which has been taken up. Too much haste will probably not produce the most desirable solution. On the other hand, most meetings are under a time limit. If they were not, the members would become bored and frustrated with a meeting that lasts too long. It is the chairman's job to give every member a chance to participate and to voice his suggestions and opinions. This is especially important when the committee members are to execute the solution of the committee. Often the chairman has to use persuasion to induce a minority to go along with the decision of the majority, and on other occasions he might have to persuade the majority to make concessions to the minority. All of this takes time, and may result in a compromise which does not necessarily represent the best possible solution. Obviously, all of this challenges the chairman's capabilities to the greatest extent.

The variations of the chairman's role run anywhere from the one extreme of an autocratic chairman to the other extreme, the most democratic counterpart. At times it is necessary even for the most permissive, democratic chairman to use tight control over the meeting, and at other occasions he may employ the loosest sort of control.

Should the chairman express his opinion? It has often been stated that the function of a good chairman is to help the members of the group reach their own decisions, to work as a catalyst to bring about the ideas present among the members of the meeting. There is no doubt that if the chairman expresses his views the members of the committee may hesitate to argue with him; this is particularly so if the conference leader is their boss.

Then again, there are occasions where it would be unwise and completely unrealistic for the chairman not to express his views. He may have some factual knowledge or sound opinions, and the value of the deliberations would be lessened if they were left unknown to the members of the committee. On the other hand, if the conference leader is also their boss, the voicing of his opinion will make it difficult for some members of the group to freely express their opinions, especially if they are in disagreement with the conference leader's opinions. But on the whole, it is best for him to express his opinions, at the same time clearly letting it be known that he is willing to subject his opinion to constructive criticism and suggestions. After all, silence on the conference leader's part, especially if he is the boss of the group, may be interpreted to mean that he cannot make a decision himself or that he does not want to do so for fear of assuming responsibility. On various occasions the chairman must use his sensitive judgment as to whether or not and to what extent he will express his own opinion.

Leadership There also is the question as to how much of a formal leadership role the chairman is to display. It has often been said that if the group of participants consists of mature members of the highest administrative echelon, no formal chairman is really necessary. Although this may be true within such a group on this level, normally there is need for a stable structure and the strong leadership of a formal chairman. If the group has a formally elected or appointed chairman they will look to him as the one to keep the work of the meeting going along so that it will come to an efficient conclusion of the problem. Under most situations the formal leadership of the chairman is important for making group discussion effective.

THE AGENDA   The best means of keeping the meeting from wandering off into a discussion of irrelevant matters is a well-prepared agenda. The chairman must carefully outline his overall strategy, his agenda, before the meeting. Topics to be discussed should be listed in the proper sequence, and often it is advisable to set up a timetable. Establishing an approximate time limit for each item assures better control of the situation. If possible, this agenda should be distributed before the meeting so that the members can better prepare themselves for the coming discussion. Although the agenda designs the overall strategy, it must not be so rigid that there is no means for adjusting it. The chairman should apply the agenda with a degree of flexibility, so that if a particular subject requires more attention than originally anticipated, the time allotted to some other topic can be reduced. Staying close to the agenda will be one of the best means of preventing irrelevant discussion. On the other hand, the chairman must not be too quick to rule people out of order. What seems irrelevant to the chairman may be important to some of the members. As a matter of fact, some irrelevancies at times actually help to create a relaxed atmosphere and to relieve tension which has built up.

Since it is the chairman's job to keep the meeting moving along toward its goal, it is a good idea for him to pause at some point during the meeting to consult the agenda, and remind the group of what has been accomplished and what still remains to be discussed. As time goes on the conference leader will learn when the opportune time has arrived to summarize one point and to move on to the next point in the agenda. If past experience tells the supervisor that his meetings have a tendency to run overtime, it might be advisable to schedule them shortly before the lunch break or just before quitting time. This seems to speed up meetings; somehow the participants seem to run out of arguments around those hours of the day.

GENERAL PARTICIPATION IN THE DISCUSSION   After a few introductory remarks and social pleasantries, the chairman should make an initial statement of the problem to be discussed. This will open up an opportunity for all members of the meeting to participate freely in an unrestricted discussion. To discuss a subject freely means that all participants may bring out those aspects of the problem which to them seem important regardless of whether or not there is any relevance to the point of discussion. Sooner or later the discussion will simmer down to those points which are relevant. There are always some members at the meeting who talk too much and others who do not talk enough. One of the chairman's most difficult jobs is to encourage the latter to speak up and to keep those who talk too much from doing so. This does not mean that all members of the meeting must participate equally. Of course, there are some who know more on a given subject than others, and some have stronger feelings about an issue than others do. But the chairman should do his best to stimulate as much overall participation as possible. The chairman's general attitude with regard to participation is important. He must accept everyone's contribution without judgment and must create the impression that he wants everyone to participate. He may have to ask controversial questions merely to get the discussion and participation started. The supervisor should ask provocative, "open end" questions, meaning questions which ask why, who, what, where, and when. Questions that can be answered with a yes or no should be avoided. Another technique is to start at one side of the conference table and ask each member in turn to express his thoughts on the problem. This has the disadvantage that instead of participating in the discussion spontaneously whenever there may be a need, the rest of the group will tend to sit back and wait until called on. But the skilled chairman will watch the facial expressions of the different people in the group. This may very well give him a clue as to whether or not someone has an idea but is afraid to speak up.

If the meeting is made up of a large number of participants, it may be advisable to break it up into small groups, commonly known as "buzz sessions." Each of the small subgroups then must report back to the meeting after a specified period of time. In this way those people who hesitate to say anything in a larger group will be more or less forced to participate and to express their opinions. Buzz sessions are usually advisable whenever the group of participants is large.

It may happen that a supervisor who is inexperienced at holding meetings is so anxious to have someone say something that there will be a lot of discussion for discussion's sake. It often happens that the most talkative member of the group may take over the whole meeting and that the other participants who may have good ideas but who are not inclined to say much do not get a chance to do so. There are ways and means for the chairman to cope with the one member who talks too much. After the speaker has had enough opportunity to express his opinion, it may be wise to conveniently overlook him and not recognize him, giving someone else the chance to speak. It might also help to ask him to please keep his remarks brief. Or arrange his seat on the conference table in a blind spot where it is easy not to recognize his request to have the floor. Most of the time, though, the other members of the meeting will quickly find subtle ways of censoring those members who have too much to say.

Once a problem has been pretty well narrowed down and understood in the same sense by all members of the group, it is advisable to get to the facts in as objective a manner as possible. Once all the facts which are relevant have been ascertained, the next logical step for the group is to suggest alternative solutions. From this point the group will go through the decision-making process as outlined in one of the previous chapters. The chairman knows that the best solution can only be as good as the best alternative which was considered. He will make certain that no possible solution is overlooked, and thus he will urge the members of the meeting to contribute as many alternatives as they can possibly think of. The next step is to evaluate the alternative solutions and to discuss the advantages and disadvantages of each proposal. In so doing, the discussion sooner or later can be narrowed down to one or more alternatives on which general agreement can be reached. Then it may be advisable to eliminate the other alternatives by unanimous consent. Some alternatives may remain which must be discussed thoroughly in order to bring about a solution. The chairman must try to play the role of a middle man or conciliator by working out a solution which is acceptable to all members of the group, possibly even persuading some discussants that their opinions are wrong. The best procedure probably would be to arrive at a solution which is a synthesis of the desirable outcomes of the few remaining alternatives. By process of integration all important points are incorporated into the most desirable solution. In so doing the chairman has the difficult job of helping the minority to save face. It is easier to achieve this if the final decision with which the group comes up incorporates something of each person's ideas so that everyone has a partial victory. Of course this can be a long and tedious process, and there is also a likelihood that the solution at which the meeting arrives may not always be the strongest solution.

It can also happen that the supervisor, as chairman of the meeting, will sense that he is confronted by a group which is hostile. In such a situation it is necessary to find out what is bothering the group, to bring their objections into the light, and discuss them. It is not uncommon that participants in a committee meeting are likely to think first of what is objectionable with the new idea rather than to think of its desirable features. Once the objections have been clarified then they can be discussed. It is conceivable that such a discussion will clarify unwarranted fears and objections, and they may be even strong enough to void the proposition.

TAKING A VOTE   The chairman is often confronted with the problem as to whether or not a vote should be taken, or whether or not he should keep on working to a final unanimous agreement regardless of how much time it would take. Offhand, many people would say that voting is a democratic way to make decisions. But on the other hand, voting accentuates the differences among the members of the group and once a man has publicly committed himself to a position it is often difficult for him to change his mind and yet save face. Also, if he is a member of the losing minority he cannot be expected to carry out the majority decision with great enthusiasm. Therefore, wherever possible it is better not to take a formal vote and to work toward a unanimous agreement.

As pointed out above, the disadvantage of working toward unanimous agreement is that such a meeting may last a very long time, and unanimity may cause serious delay. It also is true that for the price of unanimity the solution often simmers down to a common denominator and may not be as ingenious and bold as it would have been otherwise. It will depend on the situation and the seriousness of the problem involved whether or not the chairman should seek unanimity of the solution. In most instances it is not too difficult to come up with a unanimous decision. The skilled chairman can usually sense the feeling of the meeting, and all he should do then is say that it seems to him that the unanimous feeling of the meeting is that such and such be the solution.This he should do whenever possible, without taking a formal vote. In this connection it should be pointed out that observing parliamentary law is seldom of much value in small committee meetings. Of course, this does not apply to a large meeting. In that case, the observance of parliamentary procedure saves time and keeps the meeting from becoming unwieldy.

SUMMARY   There probably is no supervisor who has not been involved in committees either as a member of one or as the organizer of one. Obviously, the advantages of committees are to a degree offset by some limitations and shortcomings, and one of the more important limitations of a committee is that responsibility cannot be pinned to any individual member of the committee. In spite of the many criticisms leveled against committee meetings, they can be of great value if properly appointed and properly managed. The increasing complexities of today's society make more and more committees necessary, and it is therefore essential for the supervisor to familiarize himself with the workings of a committee. Committee meetings are called either to disseminate some information or to discuss a topic. If a topic is the subject of discussion there should be a distinction made between whether the committee is to decide the question on hand and take action based on this decision, or whether it is to make some recommendations to the line manager who appointed the committee. Regardless of the purpose of the committee, it is likely that out of these deliberations a more satisfactory and acceptable conclusion is achieved. If the committee's job is to decide a problem, the decision will be carried out with more enthusiasm by the participants than if it had been handed down by a line superior. In the composition of a committee it is essential that as many interested parties as possible are represented. These should be people who are capable of presenting their views and of integrating their opinions with those of other members. As to the size of a committee, it is advisable that there be enough members to permit thorough deliberations, but not so many as to make it bulky and cumbersome.

The success of committee deliberations largely depends on effective conference leadership. In this respect the chairman's ability and familiarity with effective group work will make the difference between successful and wasteful committee meetings. The chairman's job is to produce the best possible solution in the shortest amount of time with the greatest amount of unanimity. In trying to achieve this he is constantly faced by the problem of either running the meeting too tightly or too loosely. If his control is too tight he may frustrate the natural development of ideas, may force conclusions before all alternatives have been considered, and in general create resentment. If his control is too loose he may give the members of the meeting the feeling of aimlessness and confusion. In short, he must strive to be a "wonder boy" in order to achieve effective conference leadership.

PART IV

STAFFING

12

THE SUPERVISOR AND THE PERSONNEL DEPARTMENT

The staffing function of the supervisor includes the selection, placement, development, training, and compensation of his subordinates. It is the supervisor's function to hire, place, develop, and train the employees of his department. It is the supervisor's job to evaluate and appraise the performance of his employees, to promote them according to their effort and ability, to reward them, and, if necessary, to discipline or even discharge them. He must see to it that his subordinate employees are appropriately compensated for the jobs they perform in his department. Only if the supervisor performs all of these functions can it be said that he is fulfilling his managerial staffing duties. In checking the above list of activities many supervisors may be inclined to think that many of them are more properly the duty and activity of the personnel director and the personnel department. As a matter of fact, in reality, some of the above-mentioned activities in many hospitals and related health facilities are performed by the personnel department. Although this may be so, good management considers them the supervisor's functions, belonging to no one else.

THE STAFFING FUNCTION AND THE PERSONNEL DEPARTMENT

In all of our discussion it is assumed that within the organizational structure of the institution the personnel department is considered a staff department as defined in our discussion of line and staff. The usefulness and effectiveness of the personnel department depends largely on its ability to develop a good working relationship with line supervisors and on the quality of the line-staff relationship that exists. Much of this, of course, depends on how clearly and how specifically the administrator has outlined the areas of activities of the personnel department. In order to have effective relationships between the personnel department and the various line supervisors it is necessary to understand the appropriate function of the personnel department.

HISTORIC PATTERN The personnel department started primarily as a record-keeping department. As such it kept all employment records for the employees and managers of the enterprise, all correspondence pertaining to their hiring, application blanks, background information, date hired, various positions held within the enterprise, dates of promotions, and salary changes, leaves of absences granted, disciplinary penalties imposed, and other kinds of information which describe the employee's relationship to the hospital. The proper maintenance of these clerical records is of great importance, especially due to the growing emphasis on pension and insurance programs, seniority provisions of all kinds, and promotional and development programs. By assigning all these clerical service activities to the personnel staff, the administrator knows that they will be handled with high technical competence and efficiency, due to the specialization of the department. If such a service were not provided by the personnel department, each and every supervisor would have to keep these records within his own department. Obviously, this would be a cumbersome and time-consuming task with which to be burdened in addition to the daily chores of getting the job done. Therefore, the supervisors are happy to have the personnel department perform these services for them. The line supervisors are not very much interested in doing this work themselves, and very often may not even have the ability to do so.

148

Most personnel departments started out primarily as such record-keeping departments. Then, as time went on, mainly during the 1920s, many managers in industry felt that the threat of unionization might be thwarted if efforts were made to give employees cafeterias, better rest rooms, bowling teams, company stores, etc. Although most of those benefits have a strong flavor of "paternalism," management thought that in so doing they could make their employees happier and less resentful in the existing company setup. Since none of these activities fitted into the regular line departments of the enterprise, the personnel department took the responsibility for an increasing number of various activities such as those described above. Then, during the 1930s, another shift of emphasis took place. With the rising increase of union activities, the personnel department was expected to take direct charge of all employee and union relations. It often assumed full responsibility for hiring, firing, handling union grievances, and all other labor problems. In other words, management thought that by having a personnel department all personnel questions could be handled by them, leaving the line supervisors to go on with the job. This led to serious difficulties.

The duties and power of the personnel department increased significantly, whereas, at the same time, the standing of the supervisor as a manager of necessity decreased. The more power the personnel director acquired, the weaker the supervisor's relationship became with his own employees. The demoralized supervisor justifiably complained that he was supposed to run his department without having the power to select, hire, discipline, and reward his employees. Under those conditions it was impossible for a line supervisor to exercise effective leadership within his department. The employees no longer looked to the supervisor as their boss. They considered someone in the personnel department as boss because they were hired by the personnel department, their wages were set, and they were promoted by them. They received increases from the personnel department, disciplinary measures were meted out by the personnel staff, and firing was done by them. Under those conditions, of course, it is understandable that the employees did not look to their line supervisor within the department as the one with authority, although the supervisor did have all the responsibility of getting the job done. Since this obviously led to a bad state of affairs in many organizations, good management now necessitates a clear demarcation between the functions of the personnel department in a staff capacity and the supervisor's role as a manager of his department.

PRESENT PATTERN   Sound management principles and practices firmly advocate that staff groups, like the personnel department, should restrict their activities to advising and counseling the line supervisors who request their help. The job of the personnel manager is to provide the line supervisor with all possible services as outlined above, to be always available for advice and counsel concerning personnel problems, and to help the line supervisors in every possible respect. Going beyond this would lead to a fragmentation of the supervisor's job, would be violating the principles of management, and would make it impossible for the supervisor to be an effective manager within his department. Naturally, the line supervisor should take full advantage of the expert advice and assistance which is available within the personnel department; but the line supervisor must retain the basic responsibility for managing his department. The supervisor and personnel must work together, and their activities must interlock. But their roles and areas of authority should not be permitted to shift. Since it is the supervisor's job to get out the work within his department, he must make the managerial decisions which concern the people who work under him.

As stated above, the supervisor and the personnel department must work together and their activities must intertwine. Broadly speaking, this means that it is up to the supervisor to define the specific qualifications he expects from an employee who is to fill a specific position. It is the supervisor's job to define what the necessary capabilities for performing a particular job are. It is the personnel department's function to develop sources of qualified applicants within the local labor market. This means that the personnel department must be acquainted with the various sources within the community; the personnel department must know where to turn in order to find certain employees. The personnel department must let the community know what jobs are available and, in general, create an image of the organization as an employer. The personnel department can accomplish this by carefully planned community relations, recruiting in high schools, training schools, colleges, and other sources of employees. The personnel department should conduct preliminary interviews with those who apply, to determine whether or not their qualifications match the requirements as defined by the supervisor. They will be screened as to whether or not they meet the job description's standards, and if possible employment would comply with the law. The personnel department will make the necessary reference checks as to previous employment and past records. Those applicants who do not meet these requirements are quickly screened out, whereas those candidates who meet the stated requirements are then referred to the supervisor. It is up to the supervisor to interview, select, and hire from among those candidates whom he considers best for the position. The supervisor does the hiring—no one else. The supervisor assigns the new employee to a specific job, and it is his responsibility to judge how he can best utilize this new employee's skills to the maximum potential. It is the personnel department's job to give the new employee a general indoctrination about the hospital, about the benefits, general hospital rules, shifts, hours, etc. But it is the supervisor's job to introduce the employee to the specific details of his job—wages, departmental rules, hours, rest periods, etc. It is the supervisor's job to arrange the compensation with him. It is the supervisor's job to instruct and train the new employee on the job. It is the supervisor's duty to follow up and check the employee's performance to determine, as time goes on, whether or not he should be promoted into a better job, transferred, or discharged. During all the time an employee is with the organization complete records on him are kept by the personnel department. If the need should arise it is clearly the supervisor's duty to take disciplinary measures, and, if necessary, even to fire the employee.

Throughout the supervisor's staffing function he will be greatly aided by the personnel department, since they maintain all the clerical services for him, keep the records, and are there to provide advice, counsel, and guidance in the many personnel problems. Our basic premise is that the supervisor, in making his decisions, can follow or reject or alter the personnel department's advice and counsel. In reality, of course, it is often difficult to draw such a fine line of distinction between advice, information, and the supervisor's decision-making.

The following example will illustrate how blurred the distinction is between providing information, giving advice, and the supervisor's decision. If the staff man merely provides information, he furnishes the facts which help the supervisor make a sound decision. For instance, he advises the nursing supervisor that the going rate for nurses in the current market is so much per month. Or he may say that the current rate is so much per month, but that if the nursing supervisor were to hire the nurse at that salary she is likely to have some dissatisfied older employees in the department. In the latter remark the staff is providing not only information but also advice. By selecting the facts carefully and by phrasing his advice, he may actually sway the line supervisor's decision one way or the other. He may even advise paying the new nurse X amount per week for that particular job. And before anyone realizes it, the information becomes advice and the advice becomes a decision. This may have come about not because of a desire on the personnel man's part to broaden his authority or to reduce the supervisor's authority: the line supervisor himself may have encouraged this growth of staff activity.

Often the supervisor welcomes the personnel man's willingness to help him out in a difficult situation in order to relieve himself of some unpleasant responsibility. Many a supervisor frequently asks the personnel man to make a decision for him so that he won't have to worry about the personnel problem and can get on with his own job within his department. He gladly accepts the staff man's decision because he feels that if the decision is wrong, he can always excuse it by saying that it was not his decision but that of the personnel man. In other words, the line supervisor is only too ready to capitulate to the personnel man in many instances. It is understandable that the supervisor is often reluctant to disregard the suggestion of the staff man since the latter is the specialist for personnel problems. It is a pleasant relief for the supervisor to be able to fall back on the personnel staff's suggestion and advice, and consider it a decision. In so doing he can "pass the buck" to the personnel department.

Although it is understandable that the supervisor is reluctant to question and disregard the advice of the staff expert, the supervisor must bear in mind that the staff man sees only a small part of the entire picture. The staff man is not responsible for performance of the department. There usually are many other factors involved in the overall picture which will affect the department, factors with which the staff man is not as familiar as the line supervisor. The supervisor cannot separate his functions between clear areas of personnel problems and performance problems. Every situation has certain personnel implications, and it is impossible to separate the various components of each problem within the department. Only the supervisor is likely to know what the broader situation is.

If the supervisor capitulates and has the personnel department make the decisions for him his relationship to his employees will sooner or later be damaged. His workers will decide that it is the personnel department and not the supervisor who has the real power which will influence their job within the hospital. The supervisor's leadership position will slowly deteriorate if his employees detect that the personnel staff determines what the rate of pay is, who is hired and who is fired. They will find out that the supervisor does not control the rewards and penalties and that, in reality, he does not make the decisions in the department. The supervisor must make it clear that it is he who makes the decisions and takes the responsibility for them. There are occasions when it would be convenient to "pass the buck" but it sooner or later will backfire. Many supervisors have said that they would gladly give their employees a certain raise but that "they" (the personnel department) will not let them do so. This may be expedient for the moment, but practices of this type sooner or later lead to erosion of the supervisor's authority. It is up to the supervisor to make managerial decisions and to take the responsibility for them, regardless of the difficulty or risks involved. He is the only boss in his department.

At times a supervisor may see the necessity of discharging an employee, whereas the personnel department "advises" him not to do so. If in the future this particular employee's performance leads to additional difficulties within the department, the supervisor is apt to shrug off his responsibility by merely saying that he wanted to fire the person a long time back, but that the personnel man "advised" him not to do so. The supervisor is thus disclaiming all responsibility for this particular employee, and all of this leads to untenable conditions within a department.

THE SUPERVISOR'S STAFFING FUNCTION

The staffing function is a continuous one for the supervisor and not something which he does only when the department is first established and never thereafter. As a matter of fact, it is much more realistic to think of staffing as a situation where a supervisor is put in charge of an existing department with a certain number of employees already in it. Although there is a nucleus of employees to start with, it is likely that before too long changes will take place either due to separations of the work force or other reasons. Since every supervisor is dependent upon his employees for the results in the department, it is his duty to make certain that there is a supply of well-trained employees to fill the various positions. The amount and quality of the work performed depends to a large extent upon the abilities that the employees bring to the job.

DETERMINING THE NEED   In order to make certain that the department can perform the jobs required of it, the supervisor would do well to determine what the need for employees will be for his department. This includes both number and kind. In setting up the structure of the department, the supervisor has tentatively designed an organization structure wherein the functions and jobs are shown in their proper relations. If the supervisor takes over an existing department he will do well to orient himself by drawing a picture of the existing jobs and functions within his department. For example, the supervisor of the maintenance department finds that he has a group of painters, a group of electricians, carpenters, and persons with many other skills within his department, or should have them within his department. Then he should check within each of these skills to determine how many positions there are or should be, and in what relation they should be working to each other. In determining the needs of his department, the supervisor may often have to compromise by adjusting the ideal setup to existing necessities,

154

or by combining several positions into one if there is not enough work for one employee to perform only the one function. But only by studying the organization of the department can the supervisor determine what employees are needed to do what.

JOB DESCRIPTION   In order to fill the various positions with the appropriate employees it is necessary to match the jobs available in the department with individuals. This can only be done with the help of job descriptions. The job description tells exactly what the job contains, what the duties and responsibilities are. It describes the content of the job by listing as completely as possible every duty and responsibility involved. In many instances the supervisor will find a set of job descriptions available to him. If none are available, he will find the personnel director of great help in drawing them up. But no one is better equipped to describe the content of a job than the supervisor himself. After all, it is he for whom the employee works. It is the supervisor who is responsible for the accomplishment of the tasks of the department, and he above everyone else knows or should know the content of each position. Although the final form of the job description may be prepared in the personnel office, it is the supervisor who determines what goes into it.

Only by describing the job requirements in great detail is it possible to describe what a worker must know before he can do a job. Only then is it possible to describe the skills which are necessary in order to perform the job skillfully. It is therefore necessary to describe the content of the job in great detail and with specifics. If the position is one that is already in operation, it is still advisable to follow this procedure of determining the major duties and responsibilities. After this has been done it will be advisable to compare this list with the current job description and what the employee does. It is conceivable that the older job description no longer fits the content of the job, and should be corrected. Or the supervisor may find that some of the duties assigned to the job really do not belong to it. If the job in question is a new one then the supervisor will proceed along similar lines. He should decide what the duties and responsibilities of the job are, and with the help of the personnel department draw up a job description. Once the content of the job has been specified, the supervisor should then specify the knowledge and the skills which are required of the potential employee who applies for this particular job assignment.

In every job there are certain things an employee must know before he can perform his job appropriately. For example, in order to do the job properly it may be necessary to be able to read simple blueprints. Or the employee should be familiar with mathematics. But simply stating that a knowledge of mathematics is required for a certain job might be incorrect. The word "mathematics" could imply knowledge far beyond, say, a working knowledge of simple arithmetic, which might be all that is required in the job. The more definitely the required job knowledge is described, the easier will it be to find the person who possesses it.

In order to fulfill the content of the job it is necessary to possess certain skills in addition to a certain degree of job knowledge. No one is in a better position to describe what skills are necessary than the supervisor himself. The supervisor should caution himself not to ask for a higher degree of skill than is absolutely necessary. One way to avoid requiring unnecessarily high job knowledge and job skill is to check the requirements drawn up with the qualifications of employees who are doing the same or similar kinds of work. Such investigation may quickly reveal that for a certain job, a high school education is not necessary. The supervisor may discover that an older person with average intelligence can perform this kind of work and it is not necessary to have someone between twenty and thirty years old. The supervisor should realize that by setting employment standards unrealistically high the task of finding the person to meet these specifications will become more difficult, and unnecessarily so. There is no need to specify a certain number of years of schooling and a certain number of years of experience if all that is required is simple job know-how. This does not mean that the job specification should ask for less than what is actually needed. All it should do, however, is to specify the requirements realistically. If the requirements are set too high and people are put on the job who could meet requirements much higher than the job needs, then the likelihood is that that particular employee may prove to be troublesome because he will find that his capacities are not completely utilized. By the same token, it is just as disastrous to ask for less than necessary. Once put on the job the employee probably would turn out to be unsatisfactory. Many of these difficulties can be eliminated if the supervisor analyzes the job content diligently and specifies the job knowledge and the job skills required realistically.

The personnel department will prove to be of great help in drawing up these job descriptions. But the supervisor should be cautioned not to turn over the job of doing this to the personnel man. The content must definitely be specified by the supervisor and by no one else. Once these job descriptions have been drafted the supervisor is likely to go over them with some of the people who are holding these jobs, to make a comparison of whether or not the descriptions adequately describe the position in question. Once all difficulties have been ironed out, then these job descriptions are kept as a permanent record in the personnel department and also in the supervisor's file. Thus, whenever the supervisor needs an employee for a certain job all he has to do is to tell the personnel department that such and such a job is open and the personnel man will try to recruit suitable applicants to fill this job. The personnel man can quickly screen out those applicants who are obviously unfit because they do not have the knowledge or necessary skills or cannot fulfill any of the other requirements. But all of those who seem to fulfill the requirements will be referred to the supervisor for his acceptance or rejection.

HOW MANY TO HIRE   Normally, the supervisor is not confronted with the situation where a great number of employees for his department have to be hired at the same time. Such a situation could exist when a new department is created and the supervisor has to set about the job of staffing it completely from scratch. It is much more usual that the question of hiring an employee will turn up only occasionally. Of course, there are some supervisors who continuously ask for additional employees in order to get a job done. In most of these cases their problems are not solved even if they get more help. As a matter of fact, the situation may become worse; and instead of reducing the supervisor's problems they are actually increased.

Normally, a supervisor will need to hire a new employee when, in the usual course of activities, one of his employees leaves the employment of the enterprise either due to voluntarily quitting or to dismissal or due to some other reason. In such an instance there is little doubt that the job must be filled unless changes in the technical nature of the position have taken place. In the latter case a replacement may not be needed since the job will likely be abolished. But normally, in such a case a new employee has to be hired.

There are other situations when additional employees have to be introduced into the department, especially if new duties are to be undertaken and no one within the department possesses the required job knowledge and skill. Under those conditions the supervisor has to go out into the open market and recruit an employee. In these two instances there probably will not be any budgetary problems as the expenditures for the wages of these employees are included in the budget. Sometimes a supervisor is inclined to ask for additional help if his work load is increased or if he finds himself under added pressure. Before he ever requires additional employees under those conditions, he will do well to make certain that the persons currently in the employ of the department are fully utilized and that additional workers are absolutely necessary.

If there are vacancies within the department the supervisor should inform the employment department accordingly, and the personnel manager in turn should see to it that a number of suitable candidates for the jobs are made available. This is done by the personnel department, by consulting the various job descriptions. Those applicants who are obviously undesirable and unfit for the position in question can quickly be screened out. Those who seem to be generally acceptable and fulfill the knowledge and skills required will be passed on to the supervisor to hire or not. The decision to hire is not to be made in the personnel office; it is to be made by the supervisor in whose department the employee is to work. Although the supervisor may feel that this is not necessary in filling an unskilled job, he would be doing wrong if he would give up his prerogative and duty to hire the people who are to work in his department. It does not matter if it is a nonskilled, skilled, or semiskilled job which is to be filled. It is up to the supervisor to hire the employee. Of course, by having all of these applicants prescreened by the personnel office, the supervisor knows that all of those who are sent to him possess the minimum qualifications which are prescribed for the job. It is the supervisor's job to pick out the one who will probably fill the job best. This is not an easy task, but as time goes on the supervisor will gain more and more experience and it will become easier for him to make better decisions.

SUMMARY   Staffing is one of the managerial functions every supervisor has to perform. It means to hire, train, evaluate, promote, discipline and appropriately compensate the employees of his department. All of this is the supervisor's line function. In fulfilling this duty he is signficantly aided by the services of the personnel department. In most enterprises the personnel department is attached to the organization in a staff capacity and its purpose is to counsel, advise, and service all other departments of the enterprise. In its eagerness to be of service to the line manager, the personnel department may be inclined to take over line functions such as hiring, disciplining, setting wages, and so on. The supervisor must caution himself not to capitulate any of his line functions to the personnel department although at times it might seem expedient to let them handle the "dirty" problems.

Before the manager can undertake the staffing function he must clarify the kind of employees needed in the department and how many. The organization chart, in connection with job descriptions and job specifications, will specify the kinds of workers necessary to fill the various jobs. In addition to this, the supervisor must determine the number needed depending on the amount of work to be performed. In all of this he should call on the help of the personnel department. But it is his function to hire the employees, regardless of the importance of the job.

13

SELECTION, INTERVIEWS, APPRAISAL, AND PROMOTIONS

After all of the preliminary work has been performed by the personnel manager it becomes the supervisor's job to see the applicants, talk to them, and to select the one who will best fill the job which is vacant. This is a decisive step for the employee and for the supervisor. This is the moment when the supervisor must match the applicant's ability with the demands the job makes, with the strain of the working conditions, and the rewards it offers. This interview is an essential part of the selection process. It is not an easy task to make an appropriate appraisal of someone's potential during a brief interview. Assuming that there are several applicants for the position, it is the supervisor's job to try to find the most acceptable one among those who have not been eliminated by the personnel department for obvious deficiencies. Interviewing is much more than a technique, it is an art which can and must be developed by every supervisor.

INTERVIEWS

During the years of his experience the supervisor will learn that there are all kinds of interviews in the normal course of events in any enterprise. There are interviews between the supervisor and his employees when he hires them, there are discussions when they are fired, there are interviews during which the employee is counseled as to his abilities, there are interviews and discussions pointing toward deficiencies. There are interviews as to why an employee leaves the employment of the enterprise of his own free will, there are interviews discussing the complaints and grievances, and many other problem situations. By and large, all of these can be grouped into two different kinds of interviews, namely directive and nondirective.

DIRECTIVE INTERVIEWS Normally, one understands by a directive interview a discussion wherein the interviewer knows before he starts what particular facts will be discussed, and the interviewer will try to get to the necessary information primarily by asking the interviewee direct questions and by the latter's answering them. The employment interview in which the supervisor selects one applicant in preference to the other is one of these directive interviews.

NONDIRECTIVE INTERVIEWS Although the directive interview is the only kind with which we will be concerned, it is advisable at this occasion to call the supervisor's attention to what it means to conduct a nondirective interview. This latter kind of interview is usually used in problem situations where the interviewer is eager to find out what the interviewee thinks and feels. This is the kind of interview which is employed in problem situations such as grievances and complaints, or in an exit interview which takes place after the employee leaves the institution of his own free will. The ground rule is to let the interviewee say whatever he wants to say and to let him freely express feelings and attitudes. To carry on a nondirective interview is more difficult than to carry on a directive interview. It demands of the supervisor concentrated and continuous attention without letting his mind wander. The supervisor must exert self-control and hide his own ideas and emotions during the interview. The supervisor should never express approval or disapproval even though the employee may request it of him. This may prove exasperating, but it is essential. In such a nondirective counseling interview the employee must feel free, perhaps for the first time in his life, to express how he feels about everything. The fact that the troubled employee can pour out his troubles has therapeutic value. In all likelihood as soon as he has expressed all his negative feelings, he may start to find some favorable aspects of the very same things which he has been criticizing. Thinking out his problems aloud gives the employee a chance to gain insight into his problems. In all likelihood, he will come up with some kind of answer or some course of action which he plans to take to solve his difficulties. It it essential that the employee is permitted to work through his difficulties himself without having been interrupted and without being advised by the counselor regarding the best course of action. It should come from the employee. The nondirective counseling interview is difficult to begin with, but as time goes on a good supervisor will learn to have self-control, and by good listening he will be able to grasp the feelings of the employee.

The purpose of both kinds of interview—the directive and nondirective—is to promote mutual understanding and confidence. It is an experience in human relations which should permit the interviewer and the interviewee to obtain greater understanding, and it is an art which the supervisor will do well to develop as highly as possible. In our discussion we are primarily concerned with a directive employment interview, where the supervisor is interested in getting the necessary information chiefly by asking the interviewee direct questions.

PREPARING FOR THE EMPLOYMENT INTERVIEW   Since the purpose of the directive employment interview is to collect facts and to come to a decision as to the applicant, the supervisor should prepare it as thoroughly as possible since the time he has available is usually limited. Since it is not easy to make a correct appraisal of an applicant's potential during a brief conversation, it is necessary that as much preparation as possible be made in advance.

First, it is essential that the supervisor acquaint himself with the available background information. Much information has been assembled by the employment manager, and by making good use of whatever is available the supervisor can sketch a general impression of the interviewee in advance. The application blank itself supplies a number of facts as to the applicant's age, schooling, and previous experience and other data which may be relevant. While studying the application blank the supervisor should keep in mind the job for which the applicant is going to be interviewed. If some questions arise while studying the application blank, the supervisor should write them down so that he will not forget to ask about them. There may be some questions concerning results of previous tests given by the personnel department, and any doubts in this respect should be clarified by the supervisor before the interview takes place.

Since the purpose of the employment interview is to gather information in order to make the decision of whether this applicant should be hired or not, the supervisor should prepare a schedule or a plan for the interview. The interviewer should jot down all the important items on which he has no information. He also should write down all those points on which he would like to have further clarification. Once he has written all of these key points down, he is not likely to forget to ask the interviewee about them. It is conceivable that during the interview the supervisor may be interrupted, and he might dismiss the applicant before he has had a chance to ask about those points on which he still lacks some information. Writing them down beforehand will prevent such an occurrence. Having thought out the various questions in advance, the supervisor can devote much of his attention to listening and observing the applicant instead of having to search his own mind for what else he should know. A well prepared plan for the employment interview is well worth the time spent on it.

In addition to getting background information and making out a plan for the interview, the supervisor should be concerned with the proper setting for conducting the interview. Privacy and some degree of comfort are normally requirements for a good conversation. If a private room to conduct this interview is not available, then the supervisor should at least create the aura of semi-privacy by speaking to his applicants in a corner or in a place where other employees are not within hearing distance. That much privacy, at least, is necessary. The supervisor must also make certain that he puts the applicant at ease and creates an atmosphere of leisure. The wise supervisor will think back on his own experience when he applied for a job and recall the stress and tension under which he found himself. After all, the applicant is meeting strange people who ask searching questions, and he is likely to be under considerable strain. It is the supervisor's duty to relieve this tension which is certain to be present in the applicant and possibly also in the supervisor himself. He should create a feeling of leisure by putting the applicant at ease with a brief general conversation, possibly about the weather, the heavy city traffic, the World Series, or some other general topic of broad interest. Any general topic which does not refer to his eligibility for the job will be relaxing. The applicant may want to smoke a cigarette, and the supervisor may employ any other social gesture which may come to his mind. The feeling of leisure and an informal opening of the interview is likely to put the applicant at ease and his tensions, stresses, and fears will diminish.

CONDUCTING THE INTERVIEW   After having made preparations for the interview, the supervisor is ready to conduct it with the applicant for the job. In addition to getting information from the applicant, the applicant will want to know more about the job. The interviewer should see to it that the job seeker learns enough about the job to help him decide whether he is the right person for the position. The supervisor, therefore, should discuss with him the details about the job, working conditions, wages, vacations, his fellow workers, and who his immediate supervisor would be. In so doing, the supervisor must describe the situation absolutely honestly. The supervisor must caution himself against overselling the job by telling the applicant of what is available for exceptional employees. If the applicant turns out to be an average worker this will lead to disappointments. In his eagerness to make the job look as attractive as possible, it is conceivable that the supervisor may be inclined to state everything in better terms than they actually are.

After having outlined the details, the supervisor should ask the applicant what else he would like to know about the job. If there are no questions on his part, then the supervisor should proceed to question the interviewee in order to find out how well qualified he is. The supervisor will have some knowledge as to his background from the application blank; but he will need to know how much qualification he has in relation to the specific job in question. By this time the applicant has probably gotten over much of his tension and nervousness, and he will be ready to answer questions freely. Most of this information will be obtained by the supervisor's direct questions. The interviewer should caution himself to put these questions in words which will be clear to the applicant. In other words, he should use terms which conform with the applicant's language, background, and experience. The interviewer should take care not to put questions in the form of leading questions which would suggest a specific answer. He should ask his questions in a slow and deliberate form, one at a time, in order not to confuse the applicant. The supervisor should never use trick questions as such procedure can only lead to antagonism.

All questions the supervisor asks should be pertinent and ones which are relevant to the work situation. This brings up the area of those questions which, although they are not directly related to the job itself, can become relevant to the work situation. It is essential to know if a married woman has young children and what arrangements she can make for them to be cared for. Problems of this nature, although only indirectly connected with the job, are relevant to the work situation, and therefore they are within the area of discussion. A supervisor will have to use good judgement and tact in this respect as the applicant may be very sensitive about some of the points to be discussed. By no means should the supervisor pry into personal affairs which are irrelevant and removed from the work situation, merely to satisfy his own curiosity.

SIZING-UP THE APPLICANT   The chief problem in employment interviews is often not so much getting the candidate's employment and personal history and other pertinent facts as it is how the supervisor interprets them. It is impossible for a supervisor, since he is human, to completely eliminate all his preferences and prejudices. But he should take great care to avoid some of the more common pitfalls in interpreting the facts while sizing-up a job applicant. One of the pitfalls is commonly known as the "halo" effect. This means basing the overall impression of the applicant on only a part of the total information about him and using this impression as a guide in rating all the other factors. This may work either favorably or unfavorably for him. In either event it is bad. It would be wrong to base the overall size-up of the applicant on a single factor, for instance his ability to express himself fluently. Just because he is articulate is no reason to interpret all his other qualifications as also good. A glance at the employees in the department will remind the supervisor that he has some very successful employees whose verbal communications are rather poor. Another common pitfall is that of over-generalization. The interviewer must not assume that because an applicant behaves in a certain manner in one situation he will automatically behave the same way in all other situations. There may be a special reason why he may answer a question in a rather evasive manner. It would be wrong to conclude from this evasiveness in answering one question that the applicant is underhanded and probably not trustworthy. People are apt to generalize quickly.

Another pitfall is that the supervisor will judge the applicant by comparing him with the people who are currently working in the department and wonder how this applicant is likely to get along with the other employees and with the supervisor himself. He may feel that any applicant who is considerably different from those who are working there now is undesirable. As a matter of fact, this kind of thinking may do great harm to the organization as it will only lead to uniformity and thereafter to mediocrity. This should not be interpreted to mean that the interviewer should make it his business to look for oddballs who obviously would not fit within the department. But just because he does not fit exactly into the same pattern of the other employees is no reason to conclude that he will not make a suitable employee.

Another hazard for the interviewer to avoid is that in his eagerness to get the very best person for the job the supervisor may look for qualifications which exceed the requirements of the job. Although the applicant should be qualified to fulfill the requirements, there is no need to look for qualifications in excess of these. As a matter of fact, an overqualified applicant would probably make a poor employee for a job.

The above are some of the more commonly known pitfalls in interpreting the facts brought out during an interview. The supervisor should make all efforts not to fall into these traps when assessing the qualifications of the applicant.

CONCLUDING THE INTERVIEW   At the conclusion of the employment interview the supervisor is likely to have the choice of one of three possible actions, namely to hire the applicant, to defer the decision until later, or to reject him. The applicant is eager to know which of these actions the supervisor is going to take and he is entitled to an answer. There is no particular problem if the supervisor decides to hire this applicant. Under those conditions he will tell him when to report for work and may give him some additional instructions.

It is conceivable that the supervisor considers it best to defer a decision until he has interviewed several other applicants for the same job. Under those circumstances it is necessary and appropriate for the supervisor to tell the interviewee this and that he will be notified later on. Preferably he will give him a time limit within which the decision will be made. Such a situation occurs frequently; but it is not fair to use this tactic to dismiss the applicant in order to avoid telling him the truth. There are some supervisors who do this in order to avoid the unpleasant task of telling the applicant that he is not acceptable. Telling the applicant that the supervisor is deferring action gives him false hopes, and while waiting for an answer he may not apply for another job and let some other opportunities slip by. Of course it is unpleasant to tell an applicant that he will not do for the job. But if the supervisor has decided that he will not hire a certain applicant the applicant should be told about this by the supervisor in a clear but tactful way. It is much simpler to let the rejected applicant wait for a letter which never arrives. But the applicant is entitled to an honest answer. If he does not fulfill the requirements of the job, it is preferable to tell him the reason why. Some applicants may even use this criticism in a constructive way. If the supervisor does not want to go this far, the least he should do is to tell the applicant frankly that he is not the right man for the job.

The supervisor should always bear in mind that the employment interview is an excellent opportunity to build a good reputation for the enterprise. The applicant knows that he is one of several applying for the job and that only one person can be selected. The only contact the applicant ever has with the organization is with the supervisor during the employment interview. Therefore, even if he should not get the job, the supervisor should bear in mind that the way the interview was handled will either leave a good or a bad impression of the enterprise with the applicant. It is, therefore, necessary that an applicant leave the interview, regardless of its outcome, at least with the feeling that he has been courteously treated and that he has had a fair deal. Every supervisor should bear in mind that it is his managerial duty to build as much good will and good reputation for the enterprise as possible, and the employment interview presents one of the rare opportunities to do so.

TEMPORARY PLACEMENT   It may sometimes happen that in the supervisor's opinion the applicant is not the right man for a particular job but he would be suitable for another position for which there is no current opening. The supervisor might be tempted to hold this desirable employee by offering him temporary placement in any job which is available regardless of how unsuitable it really is for him. The applicant most certainly should be informed in this respect by the supervisor. But such temporary placement frequently causes misunderstanding and disturbance. It is usually strenuous for an employee to mark time on a job which he does not care to perform, hoping for the proper job to open up. Normally, such strain causes dissatisfaction after a certain length of time, and this dissatisfaction is usually communicated to other employees within the work group. Therefore, generally speaking, interim placements are ill-advised and unsound.

PROMOTION FROM WITHIN

No organization can rely completely on recruiting employees from the outside, and organizations depend heavily on promoting their own employees into better and more promising positions. The policy of promoting from within the organization is one of the most widely practiced policies in personnel practices today. It is of considerable significance to the enterprise and to the individual employee. For the enterprise it insures an additional source of trained people for the better positions; for the employees it provides a powerful incentive to perform better. If an employee has worked for an enterprise for a period of time much more is known about him and the various attributes he may bring to a job than even the best selection processes and recruitment interviews could indicate. After all, the supervisors know this man, whereas they will not know the person they hire from the outside until he has been working for the organization for a certain length of time. There is little motivation for an employee to do a better job if he knows that the better and higher paying jobs are always reserved for outsiders. Additional job satisfaction will result when the employee knows that with proper efforts he can work himself up to more interesting, more challenging work, higher pay, and more desirable working conditions. Most employees like to know and feel that they can get ahead in the enterprise in which they are working.

WHENEVER POSSIBLE   The internal promotion policy should be applied whenever possible and feasible. There will likely be some occasions, however, when it will be neither. As a matter of fact, there are situations when strict adherence to internal promotion would do harm to the organization. For instance, if there are no qualified candidates for the better jobs available the internal promotion policy cannot be followed. If no one with the necessary skill is available then, of course, someone from the outside has to be recruited for the position. At times the injection of "new blood" into an organization may be very important as it will keep the members of the enterprise from becoming conformist and repetitious. Such a threat is primarily important in managerial jobs and less important in hourly paid jobs. Another reason the enterprise may have to recruit employees from the outside is because in some instances the organization cannot afford the expense of training new employees. A particular position may require a long period of expensive training and the enterprise simply cannot afford this kind of upgrading program. Only large firms can afford such expenses.

The supervisor should not forget, on the other hand, that not every employee wants to be promoted. There are some who do and others who are perfectly satisfied in their present position. They are quite content with what they are doing and where they are within the enterprise, and prefer to remain with the employees whom they know and the responsibilities with which they are familiar. These employees should not be coerced into better positions by the supervisor.

The supervisor should also bear in mind that what he may consider a promotion may not seem like a promotion to the employee. A nurse may feel that a "promotion" to administrative work is a hardship and not an advancement. She may find the administrative activities less interesting than the professional duties, and she may be concerned about her professional future. Such an attitude is conceivable and the supervisor will have to provide promotional opportunities which do not entail compromises of professional feelings.

BASIS OF PROMOTION   In spite of the objections stated
above, there are usually more applicants for promotions than
there are openings within the organization. It is important for a
supervisor to select a sound basis on which employees are to be
promoted. Since promotions are considered an incentive for employees to do a better job, it would follow that that employee
should be promoted who has the best record of quality, productivity, and skill. But in most situations it is difficult to objectively
measure some employees' productivity although a continuous
effort in this respect is made by supervisors in the form of merit
ratings and performance appraisals. (There will be further discussion of this later in this chapter.)

Length of service   There are many factors beyond the control
of an employee which may affect his productivity and performance, and it would be unfair to base a promotion primarily on
these factors. Since it is difficult to find objective criteria which
would eliminate favoritism and possible discrimination, it has
been stated that the only objective criterion is length of service.
Unions have put the greatest stress on seniority; and thinking of
this sort is now regularly accepted also by those enterprises which
do not deal with unions or in cases of jobs which are not covered
by union agreements. Regardless of unions, managers have
come to depend heavily on this concept of seniority as a basis
for promotion. If management is committed to promotion based
on length of service, it is likely that the initial selection procedure of a new employee will be a more careful one, and he
will get as much training as possible in his various positions.
Some managers feel than an employee's loyalty as expressed by
his length of service deserves the reward of promotion. Basing
promotion on the length of service also assumes that the employee's ability increases with his service. Although this may
be questionable and may be limited up to a certain level, it is
likely that with continued service his ability is increasing.

Merit and ability   But even most unions recognize that length
of service cannot be the only criterion for the selection for promotion. In most instances it is agreed that promotion should be
based on seniority coupled with merit and ability. In all likelihood this is a provision which most union contracts incorporate.
But even then management often has run into the difficulty of

how much more ability is necessary to make up for less seniority. It therefore frequently happens that even in those union contracts which require ability as a co-determinant for promotion, the only objective criterion which sooner or later wins out is the criterion of length of service.

Good supervisory practice will attempt to draw a happy medium between the concepts of merit and ability to do the job on the one hand and the length of service on the other. When the supervisor selects from among the most capable subordinates he will no doubt choose the one with the longest service. Then again, the supervisor may decide that the employee who is more capable but has less seniority than another employee will have to stand "head and shoulders" above the one with longer service. If this would not be so then the one with more seniority will be promoted. Obviously, these decisions become increasingly difficult and it is easy to see why many supervisors have finally resolved the matter by making length of service the sole determinant of selection for promotion. The ideal solution, of course, is to combine both factors. It is on very rare occasions that a supervisor would choose a man with the greatest merit and ability from all eligible candidates without giving any weight to his length of service.

THE PERFORMANCE APPRAISAL SYSTEM

Obviously, it is important for a supervisor to be in a position to objectively assess the quality of the performance of his employees in his department. Therefore, many organizations request their supervisors periodically to appraise and rate their employees. The performance appraisal serves a dual purpose. It is a guide for possible promotion and further development, and also a basis for merit increases. Appraisal is done with the help of a formalized system of evaluation, often also called merit rating. The purpose of such a formal rating system is to reduce to objective terms the performance, experience, and qualities of the employees as they compare with the requirements of the job. This is done by taking into consideration such criteria as cooperation, dependability, output, housekeeping, judgment, safety, and so on. Such a system of evaluation helps the supervisor to take all factors into account when considering merit increases or a promotion, and it reduces the chances for personal bias. Such a formal appraisal system forces the supervisor to observe and scrutinize the work of his subordinates not only from the point of view of how well the employee is performing his job, but also from the standpoint of what can be done to improve his performance. Since an employee's poor performance and his failure to improve may be due to the supervisor's own inadequate supervision, a formal appraisal system is bound to improve the supervisor's own supervisory quality.

But aside from these valid reasons, a formal merit rating system serves another purpose. Every employee has the right to know how well he is doing and what he can do to improve his work performance. It can be assumed that most employees are eager to know what their supervisors think of their work. In some instances the employee's desire to know how he stands with his boss can be interpreted as asking for reassurance as to his future in the organization. In other instances this expressed desire can be interpreted in several other ways. For instance, the subordinate may realize that he is doing a relatively poor job but hopes that his boss is not aware of it and is anxious to be assured in this direction. And then again, another subordinate, knowing that he is doing an outstanding job, may wish to make certain that his boss is aware of it and receive more recognition for it.

The mere existence of regular appraisals is an important incentive to the employees of an organization. It is only too easy in a large organization to have the feeling that due to the great amount of specialization the individual worker and his contribution, which necessarily is small, are forgotten and lost. With regular appraisals the employee has the assurance that there is the potential for improving himself in his position, and that he is not lost within the enterprise. It gives him the assurance that his supervisor and the entire organization care about him. Therefore, regular appraisal of all employees should be made by the supervisor routinely—at least once a year—covering all the employees in his department. One year is normally considered a sufficiently long period of time, although it has been found advisable to make an appraisal within six months if an employee has just started in a new and more responsible position. These periodic appraisals will assure the employee that whatever improvement he has made will be noticed, and that he will be rewarded for it. As time goes on, these periodic merit ratings and reviews of them will become an important basis for the employee's morale. It reaffirms the supervisor's interest in him and his continuous development and improvement.

In summary, performance appraisals are beneficial in the following ways: They help the management in the decisions of compensation. They help in the analysis of training and developmental needs for the employees. They provide inventory of human resources suitable for promotions. As to the supervisor, appraisal programs are a help since they show whether the employee is in the right job or not. They identify for him those employees who are going ahead and those who are not progressing satisfactorily. They show him whether or not he is succeeding in his job as a coach and teacher. As far as the employee is concerned, an appraisal program has many advantages. It tells him what kind of job he is doing, and gives him the sense of being treated fairly and not overlooked. He knows what he can do in order to be promoted to a better job. It gives him an opportunity to complain and to criticize; it gives him a chance to express his personal goals and ambitions. Performance appraisal consists of two distinct steps: first, the performance rating itself, and then the evaluation interview which follows.

PERFORMANCE RATING   In order to minimize and overcome the difficulties in appraising a worker, most enterprises find it advisable to use an appraisal form. These forms reduce the various elements to be measured to objective terms as much as possible. For most supervisors, therefore, performance rating is just a matter of filling out an appraisal form. These appraisal forms are prepared by the personnel department often in conjunction with the supervisor's suggestions. Although there are innumerable types of forms for the appraisal of workers available, most of these forms include factors which serve as criteria for measuring job performance, intelligence, and personality. The following are some of the factors which are most frequently found in appraisal forms for workers: supervision required, attitude, conduct, cooperation, job knowledge, safety, housekeeping, adaptability, absenteeism, tardiness, judgment, quantity, quality, and so on. For all of these factors the supervisor is given a number of choices of the degrees of achievement which he fills in. The form is usually of a "check the box" type and very simple to fill out.

In spite of the obvious simplicity of these rating blanks the supervisor will likely run into a number of difficulties while filling them out. First of all, not all raters agree on what is meant by a term such as good, excellent, or fair. It is, therefore, advisable to add a descriptive sentence to each of these adjectives, and the supervisor can pick the one which most adequately describes the employee. It is also commonly known that one supervisor can be more severe than another in grading an employee. Some are afraid they may antagonize their subordinates if they rate them low, and thus make them less cooperative. Low rating may also reflect poorly on the supervisor's own ability because it may indicate that he has not been able to get them to improve themselves. The supervisor should also caution himself not to let the rating of one factor influence him in rating the other factors. If the supervisor feels that an employee is not good in one area he is likely to rate him low on most factors. One way to avoid this "halo" effect is to rate all the employees on a single factor before starting on the next factor. In other words, the supervisor only rates one factor of each employee at a time and then goes on to the next employee for the same factor, and so on. While filling out the form, the supervisor must be careful to exclude any personal bias he may have. All of the above are possible shortcomings. But as time goes on, the supervisor will improve his ability to fill out appraisal forms.

Throughout the appraisal the supervisor should bear in mind the job the employee is to perform, and the appraisal should be made within the context of the employee's particular job. The supervisor's judgment must be based on the total performance of the employee. It would be unfair to appraise a subordinate on the basis of only one assignment which he had done particularly well or particularly badly. The supervisor must caution himself not to let random impressions of an employee influence judgment which should be based on the employee's total record of reliability, initiative, skills, resourcefulness, and capability. Still, the results are by no means perfect but they are by far more objective than any other form of evaluation could possibly be.

THE EVALUATION INTERVIEW   The second step in the appraisal procedure is the evaluation interview, which takes place when the immediate superior who has performed the evaluation sits down with his subordinate to discuss his performance. Since evaluation interviews are not easy to conduct and can lead to considerable hostility and misunderstanding if they are poorly handled, it is essential for a supervisor to acquaint himself with the best possible way of carrying out such an interview. As a matter of fact, many supervisors shy away from this duty although the entire evaluation process will lose its effectiveness if this second step is not taken.

Everything regarding general techniques of interviewing is applicable to the evaluation interview. But additional skills are necessary since it is unpredictable in which direction such interviews may go. At times it may be very difficult for the supervisor to carry through this interview, especially if the subordinate shows hostility when the supervisor discusses some negative evaluations. Positive judgments can be communicated effectively, but it is difficult to communicate criticisms without generating resentment and defensiveness. It will take much practice and insight to acquire skill in handling this evaluation interview. Therefore, many administrators provide practice sessions and role playing experiences for supervisors to aid them in effectively carrying out appraisal interviews.

Some supervisors feel that there is no need to formally review the appraisal with the subordinate because they are in daily contact with their employees and they claim that their door is open at all times. This, however, is not enough. The employee knows that he has been appraised formally, and it is understandable that he might be eager to have a first-hand report on how he made out. He also may have things on his mind which he does not want to discuss in the everyday contacts.

The appraisal interview should be held shortly after the appraisal has been performed, and the supervisor should refresh his memory regarding the reasons for the opinions which he has expressed in the appraisal. At the outset the supervisor should

175

state that the main purpose of the interview is to help the worker improve for his own benefit and that of the enterprise. It is often suggested that the supervisor even ask the employee to appraise his own performance, and to point out those areas in which the employee thinks he has done best and those aspects of his work which he thinks should be improved. This will give the supervisor a chance to refer to the progress which the worker has made since the preceding counseling interview, compliment him on his achievements, and then go into the areas which need improvement. The formula of starting with praise, following it up with criticism, and ending the interview with another compliment is not necessarily the best method. As a matter of fact, good and bad may cancel each other out and the worker may forget about the criticism. An adult, mature employee is able to take deserved criticism when it is called for. By the same token, when he merits praise he should get it. It is not always possible to mix the two together.

Since the performance interview is not only the most important part of merit rating but also the most difficult part, the supervisor should do all in his power to make certain that at its termination the employee has a good, objective view of his performance, the ways in which he can improve, and a desire to improve. Since the idea of being rated imposes some extra tensions and strains, a feeling of friendliness and the privacy of the interview is more important here than probably at any other time. The supervisor should stress the fact that everybody in the same job in the department is rated according to the same standards, and that he has not been singled out for special scrutiny. The supervisor should be in a position to document his rating by citing specific illustrations and actual instances of good and poor performance. The supervisor should be careful to relate the factors to be rated to the actual demands of the job. He must gear the rating to the present qualities of the employee's performance. This is particularly important if an employee is already doing good work and there is the temptation to leave well enough alone. These are probably the very employees who are likely to progress further than the others; to simply tell them to keep up the good work is not sufficient. These employees may not have major problems, but nevertheless they deserve thoughful counseling. Such an employee is the one who in all likelihood will continue to develop more and more. The supervisor should be specific as far as future development plans are concerned. He therefore must be familiar with the opportunities available to the employee, requirements of the job, and the employee's qualifications. But whenever discussing the subordinate's future, the supervisor should caution himself against making promises for promotion which he may not be able to keep.

Although we have assumed that every member of the department is eager to advance, this is not always the case. The supervisor will run into some subordinates who have no particular desire to advance any further. This frequently happens with women employees who do not want the prospect of added responsibility. They feel that the increase in pay and status would demand too much of their time and energy which they would like to devote to their families.

The interview should also give the employee an opportunity to ask questions so that the supervisor can answer them fully. Any misunderstanding cleared up at this time may avoid future difficulty. The supervisor should also make it clear that there will be further performance ratings and interviews, that this is a regular procedure with the enterprise. The supervisor should always bear in mind that the purpose of the appraisal interview is to get the employee to see for himself what the problems are and find solutions to them. The real success lies in the employee's ability to see the need for his own improvement and to stimulate in him a desire to do so. It takes great skill and practice for a supervisor to conduct a good evaluation interview, as it will be necessary for the supervisor to adapt his approach to the employee's reaction during the interview.

PROPER COMPENSATION

Part of the supervisor's staffing function is to make certain that the employees of his department are properly compensated. There is no doubt that in most enterprises certain wage rates and schedules exist and that the supervisor's authority is severely limited and handicapped. Nevertheless, he should do the best he can under the circumstances to see to it that the employees in his department are compensated appropriately. It is every manager's job to offer the kind of compensation which will retain competent employees in his department, and, if necessary, attract good workers from the outside. No doubt many of the wage rates and schedules have followed historical patterns and others are often accidental. For instance, the problem of personalities has frequently distorted certain wage rates. In the long run such a situation cannot be tolerated. It is the supervisor's duty to see to it that the wages paid in his department are properly aligned internally and externally. The former means that the jobs within his department are paid according to what they are worth. External alignment means that the wages offered for the work to be performed in his department compare favorably with the going rate within the community. If they do not, the supervisor knows that he will lose the most experienced workers he has, and that he will be unable to attract new ones from the outside.

JOB EVALUATION   In order to appropriately pay the various jobs within his own department, namely, according to what they are worth, the supervisor should call on the help of the personnel department to conduct a job evaluation. In such a procedure the jobs are evaluated according to various factors and an appropriate wage rate can be based on the worth of each job performed. This is a procedure with which every personnel department is acquainted and if it has not been performed at a recent date for the entire hospital the supervisor should request a job evaluation at least for his own department. Based on the results of what the jobs are worth, an appropriate wage schedule can be instituted. Of course, there will still remain some questions of what to do with those workers who are receiving either excessively high or exceedingly low salaries in relation to others. The personnel director can be helpful in solving these problems once the overall wage structure has been clarified.

WAGE SURVEY   In order to determine whether or not the rates which the department offers are attractive to outsiders, it is advisable to request the personnel department to undertake what is commonly known as a wage and salary survey. A wage and salary survey collects data on the wages paid in the community for similar jobs in those enterprises which are engaged in the same or related endeavors. In other words, it might be a wage and salary survey of all the hospitals and related health facilities of this area. Very frequently such information is already available from a local hospital association and can be obtained easily. A comparison with what is considered the going wage paid at other hospitals for similar jobs will be of great significance for the supervisor in determining whether or not his wages are properly aligned externally.

A sound wage and salary pattern is always of great concern to the administrator, a matter in which the supervisor has very little authority. Yet the fact must not be overlooked that the supervisor's awareness of inadequacies and inconsistencies will often cause the administrator to check into it. In most instances the supervisor himself will not have enough authority to make wage and salary adjustments. But it should definitely be his concern to plead his case with top administration. However, in order to make an intelligent presentation it is necessary for the supervisor to know the value of the various jobs within the department and the going rates within the community. Proper compensation of the employees, as every supervisor knows, is a significant aspect of the employee's continuing satisfaction and high motivation.

Most enterprises also provide fringe benefits for employees, such as vacations with pay, retirement plans, insurance and health services, low cost meals, etc. In general, they are incentives to do a better job. Most of these additional benefits are established by the administrator as institution-wide measures; the supervisor has probably nothing or little to do with them other than to see to it that the employees of the department understand how they operate and to be sure that each receives his fair part.

SUMMARY   There are two ways of getting employees: to hire someone from without, or to promote someone from within the organization. In hiring from without, the supervisor is aided by the personnel department, as it performs a great amount of services by recruiting and pre-selecting the most likely applicants. However, it is the supervisor's function and duty to appropriately interview the various candidates and to hire those who promise to be the best ones for the jobs which are open. In order to accomplish this purpose it is necessary for the supervisor to acquire skills of effective interviewing. The employment interview is primarily a directive interview, in contrast to the nondirective interview often encountered in the supervisor's daily work. In order for the employment interview to come to a successful conclusion, the supervisor should prepare for it adequately, by familiarizing himself with the background information, by preparing a list of points to be covered, and by providing the proper setting. An appropriate size-up of the applicant should lead to the conclusion and results of the interview.

A second important source of employees for certain positions is the reservoir of those employees who are currently with the institution by promoting them into better jobs. Promotion from within whenever possible is one of the most rewarding personnel policies any enterprise can practice. It is of great benefit to the enterprise and to the morale of the employees. Although it is difficult to clearly specify the various bases for promotion, it is normally acknowledged that a happy balance between ability and merit on the one side, and length of service on the other, should point to the one to be promoted. However, in order to be able to clearly assess the ability and the merit of the employee it is necessary that the supervisor remain continuously aware of the employee's achievements. In order to do this the supervisor must regularly appraise the performance of the employees of his department. A merit rating system consists of the process of rating the employee and of the evaluation interview which regularly takes place thereafter. Although the appraisal interview between the supervisor and the employee may prove to be a difficult situation, the entire performance appraisal system is of no use if this aspect is ignored or not carried out appropriately.

In addition to all these duties, the staffing function includes making certain that the employees of the department are properly compensated. Although much of this is out of the domain of the supervisor, it is his function to make certain that within his department there is good internal wage alignment, meaning that each job is paid in accordance with its worth and difficulties. To achieve this, a job evaluation is necessary. In addition to good internal alignment between the various jobs, it is also essential that the enterprise have a sound external alignment. This means

180

the wages paid must be high enough to attract people from without the organization in case a vacancy exists, and to prevent present employees from leaving for higher wages. In order to do this it is essential to be familiar with current rates being paid in the community in similar occupations. Such information can be obtained by wage and salary surveys conducted by the personnel department.

PART V

DIRECTING

14

GIVING DIRECTIVES

It is the job of every manager, of every supervisor, to get the work done through and with the help of his employees. Directing is the managerial function which *initiates* action. Without directing, nothing, or at best very little, is likely to be accomplished. Planning, organizing, and staffing can be considered preparatory managerial functions; the purpose of controlling is to find out whether or not the goals are being achieved. The connecting and actuating link between these functions is the managerial function of directing. This means the issuance of directives, instructions, assignments, and orders, and the guidance and overseeing of the employees.

The supervisor must stimulate action by giving directives to his employees and by supervising them as they go about their work. He should consider his directing function as a means for achieving two important objectives, namely, getting the work done and developing and teaching his employees. The most effective way to achieve such development of the employees in the department is the diligent coaching and teaching of subordinates by their immediate supervisor. The directing function includes not only the teaching function, but also the task of getting the work accomplished. Clearly, directing is not just a matter of giving orders or supervising the employees to make certain that they follow instructions. Directing means building an effective work force and motivating each member of it to perform at his best. Directing is the function of getting the employees to work willingly and enthusiastically toward the accomplishment of the enterprise's objectives. It is the function of guiding the activities of the employees so that their activities are coordinated and the employees are properly motivated to execute the directives, thus insuring the success of the institution.

Directing is the job of every manager whether he is the president of a company, a regional sales manager, the administrator of the hospital or a related health facility, or supervisor of one department. Every manager performs the directing function, regardless of the number of subordinates. The time and effort a manager spends in directing, however, will vary, depending on his level, the number of employees he has, and the other duties he is expected to perform. It is a fact that the supervisor will spend most of his time in directing and supervising. He will spend much more time at this than the administrator of the hospital. Supervision is an ever present, continued function of the supervisor and covers the day-to-day activities within the department.

The supervisor's directing function is interconnected with his other managerial functions, and they each have a bearing on one another. It is obvious that supervision is largely influenced and affected by the kind of employee whom the supervisor has selected while performing his staffing function. It is obvious that the plans the supervisor has made, and the organization which he has drawn up, have a bearing on the directing function. The controlling function is influenced by directing and by all the other functions. Directing is a continuous function, as a good supervisor never ceases to direct, guide, teach, coach his employees. In so doing every supervisor faces the problem of motivation. It is the problem of how to get the employee to work in a large enterprise in the same way and with the same amount of enthusiasm that he would display if he were working for himself, either in his own enterprise or at a hobby. Only by appropriately directing and supervising the employee will the supervisor be able to instill in him this motivation to work on this job with enthusiasm and energy.

UNITY OF COMMAND   In this connection it is advisable to recall the principle of unity of command, to which reference was
made on previous occasions. Unity of command means that in
each department there is one person only who has authority to
make the decisions appropriate to his station. It means that each
employee has a single immediate supervisor, who is in turn responsible to his immediate supervisor, and so on up and down the
chain of command. It means that a subordinate is responsible
only to one supervisor. The principle of unity of command also
means that the supervisor is the only one who can give directives
to his employees. All directives can come only from the immediate supervisor, and there should be no interference in the guiding
and overseeing of the employee by anyone else. There is a direct
line of authority from the supervisor to his subordinate, just as
there is one from the administrator to the supervisor of the department. The administrator's line extends only to the supervisor
and not to the employees of that particular supervisor. All supervision of the employees of the department rests with the supervisor of this department and must not be exercised by anyone
else. Otherwise, the principle of unity of command is violated;
no man can serve two bosses.

ORDER GIVING

Because issuing directives is such a basic and integral part
of the supervisor's daily routine, it often has been taken for
granted that every supervisor knows how to give orders. It is
frequently assumed that anybody can give orders. This is probably not so. But whether or not this is true, there is general agreement that some ways of issuing directives are much more effective than others. The experienced supervisor knows that faulty or
bad supervision can easily upset even the best laid plans, and
instead of coordination of efforts, a general state of chaos is
achieved.

To the uninitiated outsider, it may seem that some supervisors
can get excellent results even though they seem to break every
rule in the book. Other supervisors may use all the best techniques of order giving and phrase their requests in the most
courteous ways and still get only grudging compliance. The question of what is the most appropriate way for order giving depends

on the employee concerned, the particular situation, the supervisor, the way he views his job, his attitude toward people, and many other factors. There are definite techniques for giving orders, and since the supervisor's own success depends largely on the performance of his employees, it is essential for him to possess the knowledge and the skill for good directing. Since directing is the fundamental tool employed by supervisors to start activities, to stop them, or to modify them, it is essential that the supervisor is familiar with some basic characteristics which distinguish good and accomplishable directives from those which are not.

CHARACTERISTICS OF A GOOD DIRECTIVE

1. *It should be reasonable* One essential characteristic of a good directive is that it must be reasonable and that compliance can reasonably be expected by the supervisor. Unreasonable orders will not only undermine morale, but they will also make controlling impossible. This requirement of reasonableness immediately excludes orders pertaining to activities which physically cannot be done. In judging whether or not a directive can reasonably be accomplished the supervisor should not only appraise it from his point of view, but should try to place himself in the position of the employee. The supervisor should not issue a directive if the capacity or experience of the employee receiving the instruction is not sufficient to comply with the order. It can easily happen that the supervisor issues unreasonable instructions. For instance, in order to please the administrator, a supervisor promises the completion of a job at a particular time and then issues such an order without considering whether the employee who is to carry out this directive can actually do so. The supervisor should put himself in the position of the subordinate, and ask himself if compliance with such an order can reasonably be expected. Such a decision will depend greatly on all the conditions prevailing at the time. There are some borderline cases where the directive may actually be intended to stretch the subordinate's capabilities a little bit beyond what has been previously requested. In such instances the question of reasonableness becomes a question of degree. But generally speaking, a prime requirement of a good

directive is that it can be accomplished by the employee to whom it is assigned.

2. *It should be intelligible* Another requirement is that the directive should be intelligible to the employee—that he should understand it. The subordinate cannot be expected to carry out an order which he does not understand. For example, a directive in a language not intelligible to the subordinate cannot be considered an order. This becomes obvious when one thinks of an order issued in a foreign language which the employee does not understand. But the same applies if both speak the English language. This, then, becomes a matter of communication. The supervisor must make certain that the employee understands him, and it is the supervisor's duty to speak in words and forms which the employee actually understands, and not merely should understand. Instructions should be clear but not necessarily lengthy. What is clear and complete to the supervisor is not always clear and complete to the employee. Sometimes the supervisor himself has not made up his mind exactly what it is that he wants done. Here, too, it is advisable for the supervisor to project himself into the position of the employee. A supervisor cannot expect his subordinates to carry out his directives if they have not understood them.

3. *It should be worded appropriately* Every good supervisor knows that the tone and words used in issuing directives significantly affect the subordinates' acceptance and performance. A considerate tone is likely to stimulate willing and enthusiastic acceptance, which, of course, is preferable to routine or grudging acceptance or outright resignation. The effective supervisor knows that the tone should be such as to stimulate ready acceptance. Good supervisors know not to use the term "order" but, instead, different terms should be used, such as directives, assignments, instructions, suggestions, and requests.

Requests: Phrasing orders more as requests does not reduce their character as a directive, but there is a big difference in the reaction a request will inspire as compared to a command. With the majority of subordinates a request is all that is needed and commonly used. It is a pleasant and easy way of asking an employee to get the job done, particularly with those employees who have been working for the supervisor for some time and who are familiar with the personality of the supervisor, and vice versa.

A request works well with this kind of employee, and it usually does not rub him the wrong way.

Suggestion: In other instances it might be advisable to place the directive in the form of a suggestion, which is still milder form than a request. It is the kind of order where the supervisor might say, "George, we are supposed to get all of this work done today and we seem to be a bit behind. Do you think we can make up for it?" Requests of this and similar nature will accomplish a great deal for the supervisor as it will be grasped by his responsible and ambitious employees. They like the feeling of taking part in making decisions of this type, getting the job accomplished. However, this suggestive type of order would not be advisable where the supervisor is dealing with newer employees. The newer employees simply do not have the background of the department or have not been around long enough in order to have received sufficient training and familiarity with the activities. Nor will the form of suggestion be the proper way of giving orders to those employees who are incompetent and undependable.

Some subordinates must be told what to do simply because a request or a suggestion might invite an argument as to why they should not do it. Sometimes the command type of order is the only way to get things done. Everyone remembers commands from parents and schoolteachers as a part of the process of growing up. Most employees, of course, feel that now, since they are grown up, these days are gone forever. The best rule for a supervisor is to avoid the command form of an order whenever possible but to remember to use it on those occasions when it is needed.

Most directives between the supervisor and his employees are of an oral nature. Supervisors will have little occasion or need to issue written orders to employees who are carrying out their daily tasks. There may be some occasions when written orders must be issued; but normally there is no need for them in the supervisor's daily relationships with his employees.

4. Compatible with objectives A good directive must be compatible with the purposes and objectives of the enterprise. If the instructions are not in conformance with the objectives of the enterprise, the chances are that the subordinate may not execute the directives adequately, or may not execute them at all. It is

187

therefore necessary that the supervisor, when issuing directives which appear to the employee to be in conflict with the main purpose of the organizational objective, explain to the recipient why such action is necessary, or that the directive merely appears to be in conflict, but actually it is not contrary to the objectives of the enterprise. Instructions must be consistent; they must not be in opposition to orders or directives previously given.

5. *Time element* An additional characteristic of a good instruction is that it specifies the time within which the instructions should be carried out and completed. The supervisor should bear in mind that a reasonable amount of time must be allowed, and if this is not feasible, he must realize that the quality of the performance can only be as good as can be expected under the time limit. In many directives the time factor is not clearly stated, and it probably is implied that the assignment should be carried out within a reasonable length of time. What is a reasonable length of time will depend on the circumstances of the situation.

The above are some of the major characteristics which should be incorporated in a good directive. Because the performance of the employees depends to a large degree on directives given by the supervisor, the latter should make certain that his directing is in accordance with these most essential characteristics.

MAJOR TECHNIQUES OF DIRECTION

Generally speaking, the supervisor may choose from two broad basic techniques of direction running all the way from the autocratic, close supervision on the one hand, to the consultative, general supervision on the other. In a discussion of this type we can clearly distinguish between those two extremes. But in practice, the supervisor usually depends on shadings and blendings of these techniques, and the appropriate proportions and proper applications will vary, depending upon the skill and the experience of the supervisor, the subordinate in question, the situation at hand, and many other factors. However, these two basic methods of directing are at the supervisor's disposal, and it is conceivable that he might use one or another of these techniques at different times. It is also possible that for some of his employees he might consider it more advisable to use one method and for other subordinates another. No one form of supervision is equally good in all situations. Whether it is better to apply a more autocratic supervision or a general kind of directing will depend on many factors: the type of work, the attitude of the employee toward the supervisor, the occasion, the personality of the subordinate, his ability, and on the personality, experience, and ability of the supervisor, and many other conditions under the circumstances. A good supervisor is sensitive to the needs of each situation, and he will adjust his style of supervision accordingly.

AUTOCRATIC CLOSE SUPERVISION When the supervisor employs the autocratic technique of directing—close supervision —he gives direct, clear, and precise orders to his subordinates with detailed instructions as to how and what is to be done, allowing no room for the initiative of the subordinate. He gives detailed instructions telling his subordinates exactly how and in what sequence he wants things done. The supervisor who normally uses the autocratic technique of supervision is the kind of person who will delegate as little authority as possible, and who believes that in all probability he can do the job better than any of his subordinates. He relies on command and detailed instructions followed by close supervision. He is the kind of supervisor who feels that his subordinates are "not paid to think," that they are expected to follow instructions, that he alone is to do the planning and decision-making and that this is what he is trained and paid for. The autocratic supervisor does not necessarily distrust the subordinate, but he feels that without minute instruction from him the subordinate could not properly carry out the directive. He believes that only he can specify the best method and there is only one way—namely, his way—the job can be done. At the same time, he believes in close supervision of his subordinates by "breathing down their necks."

With most people the consequences of this type of supervision can be fatal. Employees lose interest and initiative, they stop thinking for themselves, because there is no need or occasion for independent thought. They are obedient but silent and lack initiative, sparkle, and ingenuity. It will become difficult to remain loyal to the organization and to the supervisor; the subordinate secretly rejoices when his boss makes a mistake. This kind of supervision tends to make the employee somewhat like an au-

189

tomaton. His freedom is curtailed and it is difficult for him to learn even by making mistakes; he justly concludes that he is not expected to do any thinking about his job, and although he perfunctorily performs his duties he finds little involvement in his work.

These shortcomings of the autocratic technique of close supervision are obvious. Generally speaking, young men and women who have been brought up in a democratic and permissive society from their early school days resent autocratic order-giving. It is contrary to our traditional democratic way of life in America. No ambitious employee will remain in a position where the supervisor is not willing to delegate some degree of freedom and authority. Any subordinate who is willing and eager to learn and to progress will resent being constantly given detailed instructions that leave no room for his own thinking and initiative. He will be stifled, and sooner or later he will leave the enterprise. This method of supervision does not produce good employees and will only chase away those who have the potential.

On the other hand, it must not be forgotten that under certain circumstances and with certain people a degree of close supervision may be necessary. But this is the exception, not the rule. The subordinate may be the kind of a person who does not want to think for himself and prefers to receive clear orders. Firm guidance gives him reassurance, whereas loose and general supervision may be frustrating to him. There are some employees who lack ambition and imagination, and do not become at all involved in their daily job. Then again, there are those employees who have been brought up in an authoritarian attitude in their families, and whose previous work experience leads them to believe that general supervision is no supervision at all. Also, there are occasions when a work situation is so chaotic that only autocratic techniques can bring order. Aside from these rather unusual situations it can generally be assumed that autocratic, close supervision is the least desirable and the least effective method.

The autocratic supervisor makes the basic assumption that the average employee does not want to do the job, that close supervision and threats of loss of job are needed in order to get people to work. He feels that if he were not on the job and "breathing down their necks" they would all stop working. And under those conditions they very likely would. However, the supervisor who believes in general supervision assumes that the average employee is eager to do a good job; that the average employee wants to do the right thing, and that the employees must have motivation to perform at their best. Obviously, autocratic, close supervision is not conducive to motivating employees to perform at their best; general supervision will.

CONSULTATIVE TECHNIQUE AND GENERAL SUPERVISION

The opposite to the autocratic, close supervision is what is commonly know as the consultative, participative, democratic, or permissive way of directing, sometimes known as general supervision. Its basic assumption is that the employees are eager to do a good job and are capable of doing so. The supervisor behaves toward them with this basic assumption in mind, and the employees, in turn, tend to react in a manner that justifies the expectations their supervisors have. This democratic, permissive approach of the supervisor in his directing function demonstrates itself in a kind of general supervision when it comes to routine assignments within the department. When new jobs have to be performed, new assignments to be made, this democratic technique of supervising will manifest itself in what is usually known as consultative or participative technique of directing. Both, of course, have the underlying assumption that the employees are eager to do a good job, that they will be more motivated if they are left to themselves as much as possible. We shall first discuss the situation when consultation is advisable and, later, the meaning of general supervision for routine assignments.

CONSULTATION   The essential characteristic of this method is that the supervisor consults with his employee concerning the feasibility, the workability, and the extent and content of a problem before the supervisor makes a decision and issues a directive. Of course, such consultation and decision are not necessary if it is a routine assignment and if no new problems are involved. When the supervisor uses the consultative or participative approach in issuing directives he is earnestly seeking help and ideas from the employees, and approaches the subject with an open mind. More important than the procedure is the attitude of the supervisor. A subordinate will quickly sense superficiality and is quick to perceive whether or not his boss genuinely intends to consult with him on the problem or intends only to give the impression of so doing.

There is a danger that some supervisors are inclined to use such a pseudoconsultative method merely to give the employee the feeling that he had been consulted. In many instances supervisors ask for participation only after they have decided on the directive, with the thought that it would be good for the subordinate to feel as if he had participated. Here the supervisor is using the consultative technique as a trick, as a device for manipulating people to do what he wants them to do. The employees, in turn, will sense very quickly what the true intentions of the supervisor are. The subordinate will sense quickly that he is not taken seriously and that his participation is not real. The results achieved will be much worse than if the superior had used the most autocratic method. In the latter instance the supervisor may be called unflattering names by his subordinates, but they cannot call him a hypocrite. If a supervisor is to practice consultative management when it comes to the issuing of new directives and new assignments, he must be ready to take it seriously and must be willing to be swayed by the employee's opinion and suggestions. If he is not sincerely willing to do so, it would be better for him to avoid its use and not apply it in the first place.

If the subject matter concerns only the supervisor and one employee, the consultative or participative method can be carried out in a most informal manner. There are numerous occasions during the day to hold such discussions. There is, of course, a danger that if the supervisor uses this approach all the time, his subordinate may begin to doubt whether or not the supervisor has any opinions of his own and is able to make any decisions. Subordinates sometimes comment that their boss does not seem to be able to ever give them any instructions or orders in a unilateral manner, and that he is too indecisive. In some instances it is probably correct that the supervisor is incapable of making a decision. However, there are other managers capable of deciding for themselves but who, nevertheless, use the consultative technique so extensively that they give their subordinates the impression that they are unable to make decisions. In such a case the supervisor, no doubt, has gone too far in the utilization of this philosophy of directing. Somehow, while implementing his technique of participation he has not been able to retain the atmosphere of managing. Although caution must be taken that the supervisor's opinion is subject to the same criticism as the suggestion of the subordinate, it is essential that in discussing the problem the manager does not hesitate to express his own opinions and solutions.

Consultative direction does not lessen or weaken the supervisor's formal authority, because the right to decide still remains with him. It should be remembered that the supervisor using this democratic approach is just as much concerned with getting the job done economically and expeditiously as the manager who uses another kind of approach. But the supervisor must not dominate the situation to the point that it excludes any participation by the employee. Nor does it imply that the supervisor cannot express his opinion. He must, however, express it in a manner which indicates to the employee that even the supervisor's opinion is subject to critical appraisal. On the other hand, it does not mean that ultimately the suggestion of the employee might not be rejected. True consultation means a sharing of the information between the supervisor and the employee and a thorough discussion of the alternate solutions regardless of who originated them. Only then can it be said that the manager consulted the subordinate.

In order for consultative practices to be successful, it is not only necessary that the supervisor be in favor of it, but the employee must also want it. If he is the kind of subordinate who believes that "the boss knows best" and that making decisions and giving directives is none of his concern, there is little likelihood that opportunity to participate will induce better motivation and better morale. In this same connection it should be kept in mind that the employee should be consulted only in those areas in which he is capable of expressing himself and in which he can draw on a certain fund of knowledge. The problems involved must be consistent with the subordinate's ability. Asking participation in areas which are outside of his scope of experience will make the employee feel inadequate and frustrated instead of motivating him.

In using consultation there is the danger that at the end of an extended discussion the employee may not have a clear and crisp idea of the solution which was arrived at. It is therefore desirable and even necessary that the supervisor or the subordinate summarize the directive in order to avoid this pitfall. This is even more essential if several employees were involved in the participation.

One of the obvious advantages of consultation is that the directive emerging therefrom does not appear to the employee as an order, but as a solution which came directly from him or in which he participated. This assures the subordinate's best cooperation and enthusiasm in carrying it out. It is needless to repeat that the morale of the employee is bound to be higher after having been asked to participate and solve the problem. In so doing he has been given a feeling of importance since it is evident that his ideas are desired and valued. Active participation provides an outlet for reasoning power and imagination and an opportunity for the employee to make a worthwhile contribution. Since there is a considerable degree of talent among employees, their ideas often prove of real value in improving the quality of the directive. An additional advantage of this technique is that it will bring the employee closer to the supervisor and it will make for better communication. They will learn to know each other better. Looking at this impressive list of advantages of the consultative technique, it becomes apparent that it is by far the best to use whenever the supervisor has to issue new assignments, new directives, and new instructions.

GENERAL SUPERVISION This democratic, permissive, participative point of view of directing subordinates leads to what is commonly known as general supervision when it comes to routine assignments and the carrying out of the daily chores involved in each employee's job. General supervision means to let the subordinate work out the details of his job, to let him make the decisions of how best to do it. In so doing the worker will find great satisfaction by being on his own and by having a chance to express himself and to make decisions on his own free will. Instead of giving a specific, detailed list of orders, general supervision means to just generally indicate to the employee what needs to be done and to make suggestions. Since the employee is well acquainted with his job, the details are left to him to work out. In so doing the supervisor assumes that, given the proper opportunity, the average employee wants to do a good job. The supervisor is primarily interested in the results and lets the subordinate decide how to achieve these results. He tells his subordinate what he wants accomplished, establishes the goals, and normally fixes the limits within which he can work. But aside from this, he lets the subordinate decide how to achieve these goals. Obviously, this kind of thinking and supervision can only lead to higher motivation, higher morale, and ultimately to a better job. It gives the employee the opportunity to satisfy his need for self-expression.

EXPLAINING WHY   The supervisor who practices general supervision creates an atmosphere of understanding and mutual confidence in which the employee will always feel free to call on his boss whenever the need arises without fear that this would indicate incompetence. By the same token the supervisor takes great pains to explain to his workers the reasons for the general directives and why certain things have to be done. By the supervisor's explaining the purpose behind the directives, the employee will be able to understand the environment of his activities. This will make him better informed, and the better informed the subordinate is the better he will perform. It is a common complaint in many enterprises that subordinates are kept in the dark most of the time and that supervisors hoard knowledge and information which they ought to pass on. In most instances it is exceedingly difficult to issue directives so completely as to cover all particulars, to leave no room for interpretation or adaptation. Therefore, if the person who receives the order knows the purpose behind it he is in a better position to carry it out than the one who does not know. It will enable him to put the environment together and to make sense out of it so that he can take firm and secure action. Without this knowledge the employee will find himself in an anxiety-producing situation. The employee may run into unforeseen circumstances, and if he knows why the directive was given he will probably be able to use his own good judgment and carry out the order in a manner that will bring about proper results. He could not possibly do this if he were not well informed.

There is an often-told story illustrating the importance of explaining why. A foreman had a crew of workers dig holes at random in the factory yard. Each time two men had dug a hole four feet deep the foreman was called over to inspect the hole, after which he ordered the men to fill it up again. After the lunch break the work crew refused to do the job as they thought it completely useless. At that point the foreman explained the purpose, telling them that the blueprints for an old water main line had been lost and that they were searching for this water main. With this explanation the workers were happy to return to their work. It is superfluous to state that the supervisor could have saved himself some extra work had he explained the reason for the job in the beginning. As each hole was dug, the worker could have searched for the water main and the supervisor could have avoided the inspection of these holes.

It sometimes happens that a supervisor, in his desire to explain, can overdo a good thing and, instead of clarifying, he offers so much information that ultimately the subordinate is utterly confused. Explanations should include only enough to give the subordinate background without confusing him. If the directive involves only a very minor activity and if not much time is available, the explanation will probably be very brief. There is another well-known story of a little girl who, at the age of four or five years, asked her daddy some of the vital questions about the facts of life which a four, five, or six year old would ask from time to time. When she asked her daddy, who really did not know what answer to give at this time, he suggested that she ask her mother. The little girl replied: "But Daddy, I don't want to know *that* much about it." Here, too, a short explanation as to the reasons why would have sufficed and stilled her interest at least for the time being. The supervisor must use his own judgment in deciding how far he will go in explaining the reasons why. This will depend on several factors such as the capacity of the subordinate to understand, the training he has had, the content of the directive, how well the employee is indoctrinated, the attitude of the supervisor, and the time available.

GENERAL SUPERVISION DOES NOT MEAN "NO SUPERVISION" General supervision is not the same as no supervision at all. General supervision requires that the employee is given a definite assignment. But this assignment is definite only as far as the results are concerned, and the employee is given to understand what results are expected of him. It is not definite regarding the specific instructions which tell him precisely how the results are to be achieved. General supervision does not mean that the subordinate can set his own standards. The supervisor will set standards which are realistic, high enough so that they represent a challenge, but still not higher than can possibly be achieved. Although general supervision excludes direct pressure, employees know that their efforts are being measured against these standards, and this thought alone will lead them to work harder. By setting these standards reasonably high the general supervisor applies a degree of pressure. But this kind of pressure is quite different from the pressure exerted by "breathing down someone's neck."

General supervision requires a continuous effort on the supervisor's part to train his employees more and more. Everyone knows that active learning is more effective than passive learning. Employees learn more easily when they work out a solution for themselves, than if they are given the solution. It is a known fact that employees learn best from their own mistakes. In general supervision the supervisor spends considerable time training his employees to solve problems and to make decisions as problems arise in their work situation. Continuous training of employees is an absolute necessity in general supervision. The better trained the employees become, the less need there will be for supervision. One way to judge the effectiveness of a supervisor is to see how the employees in his department function when he is away from the job.

Since general supervision is a way of life which must be practiced over a period of time, the supervisor cannot expect sudden results if he introduces general supervision in a situation where the employees have been accustomed to close supervision. It will take time before the results can be seen. The general supervisor is just as much interested in results as any other kind of supervisor. It is merely the method which he applies which differentiates him from the autocratic and close supervisor.

Although the supervisor may be a firm believer in general supervision and will practice it wherever he can, this does not mean that from time to time, under certain conditions, he must not show his firmness, fortitude, and decisiveness. There may be occasions and there may be certain employees who just do not seem to thrive under this kind of loose, general supervision and are in need of a closer type of supervision. It is not a cure-all to all problems. However, all indications are that general supervision is more effective than close supervision. General supervision permits the employee to acquire pride in his work and in the results which he has achieved. It helps develop the talent and capability of the subordinate. It permits the supervisor to spend less time with his employees and to spend his own time on the overall management of the department. General supervision provides the motivation for the employee to work on his job with enthusiasm and energy, thus deriving full satisfaction from his work. All research studies made in this respect seem to indicate that general supervision is more effective than close supervision in terms of productivity, morale, and achievements. But again it should be stated that there are occasions, subject matters, and employees where the supervisor simply cannot apply these democratic ways of directing and may have to resort to more autocratic procedures. This, however, should be the exception and not the rule.

DIRECTING AND THE INTRODUCTION OF CHANGES

The supervisor's directing function is a continuous function and is never finished. It is used whenever the manager is faced with the introduction of a change. Since every enterprise operates in a larger context and since the environment is of a dynamic nature, change is to be expected as a part of everyday life. As a matter of fact, the growth of most businesses depends largely on the concept of change. Most people pride themselves on being modern and up to date, and most gladly accept and welcome changes in material things, whether it be a new automobile, new design of homes, clothing, or any kind of gadgets. But when it comes to changes referring to jobs and interpersonal relations, there is a tendency to resist changes. Since changes of all types are important for the successful operation of any enterprise, it is unfortunate that most people have this tendency to resist change. If an enterprise is to survive, it must be able to react to the prevailing conditions by changing itself and by issuing directives which will incorporate and realize the necessary changes. However, since resistance to change is a common phenomenon, it is essential for the supervisor to learn about the causes for this resistance and what he can do to help his employees to accept the resulting changes.

One reason for resisting change is that change disturbs the equilibrium of the state of affairs, the situation and environment in which individuals exist. The assumption is that prior to the change the employee exists within an environment in which his need satisfaction has reached a high degree of stability and the change may prevent or decrease the satisfaction of his needs. At the outset new ideas and methods almost always represent a threat to the security of the individual involved in the change. Usually people fear change because they cannot assess or predict what the change will bring in terms of their own position, activity, and security. It makes no difference whether the change actually has this result. What matters is that the subordinate believes or assumes this.

Changes affect different people in different ways. A change that causes great disturbance to one person may create little disequilibrium for another. The type and severity of reaction which occurs in a particular situation will depend on the nature of the change and the person concerned. The important thing is for the supervisor to recognize that changes disturb the equilibrium of the employee, and that when individuals become threatened they develop ways of behavior that serve as barriers to the thing that threatens. Therefore, it is the supervisor's duty to facilitate the inevitable process of adjustment when changes are necessary, and in order to deal with these reactions the manager must understand and respect the subordinate's reaction to change.

One of the factors which is of importance in gaining acceptance of new ideas and methods is the relationship that exists between the supervisor who is trying to introduce the change and the employee who is subject to the change. If a relationship of confidence and trust exists between the two, the employee is much more likely to go along with the change than otherwise. The supervisor must communicate and explain to his employee those things which the latter consciously and subconsciously wants and needs to know in order to resolve his fears of a new situation. Only then can he assess and understand what the change would mean in terms of his own position and activity. The supervisor must help the subordinate understand the need for the change. This will be facilitated if the supervisor has always been concerned with setting the proper stage and giving the proper background information for all of his directives. In such a case the employee is thoroughly acquainted with the underlying factors, and if there should be considerable changes in any of them he will readily understand the necessity for the change. He might ask a few additional questions about it, but he then can quickly adjust to it and resume his previous behavior. When the subordinate has been informed of the reason for changes or even participates in the process leading to the new directive, he knows what to expect and why. Instead of blind resistance, there will be intelligent adaptation of the instructions, and instead of insecurity, there will be a feeling of security. In the final analysis it is not the change itself which leads to so much misunderstanding, it is more the manner in which the supervisor issues the directive for the change.

In other words, resistance to change that comes from fear of the unknown can be minimized by supplying appropriate information. This information should explain what will happen and why. It should clarify the way in which the change will affect the employee and what it means to him. It should show how the change will leave him no worse off or even improve his present situation. All of this information should be communicated to the entire department, to those employees who are directly involved and also to those who are indirectly involved.

Another effective way of reducing the resistance to change is to permit the individual or individuals affected to share in the making of the decisions. If several employees are involved, this group decision-making is an effective means for overcoming resistance to change. This approach recognizes the fact that if the employees who are threatened by a change have the opportunity to work through the new ideas and methods from the beginning and can assure themselves that their needs will be satisfied in the future, they will accept and recognize the new ideas and methods as something of their own making and will give it their support. Group decision-making makes it easier for each member of the group to carry out the decision once it is agreed upon, and the group will put strong pressure on those who have reservations or do not want to go along. Group decision-making is effective in those changes where the supervisor is really indifferent to what the group decides as long as the job gets done. For instance, the supervisor may not be interested in how a new work load is divided as long as the job is accomplished. In such a case group decision-making is the most effective way to overcome resistance to change. If the reason for resistance to change is primarily economic, which it very often is, then, of course, an economic reward is probably the best answer. In such a situation the cause of resistance has been removed.

Many supervisors are inclined to ignore the existence of resistance to change and often fail to recognize that even a trifling change may have deep reactions on the employees of the department. The supervisor should remember that employees seldom resist a change just to be stubborn. They resist because the change concerns their equilibrium socially, psychologically, and possibly economically. It is therefore necessary for a supervisor to be familiar with the ways in which resistance to change can be handled successfully.

SUMMARY   The directing function of the manager is that function which forms the connecting link between planning, organizing, and staffing on one side, and controlling on the other. Without issuing directives and without supervision nothing, or at best very little, would be achieved. The principle of unity of command dictates that every subordinate can have only one boss who may give directives to him. In order for directives to be properly carried out there are certain prerequisites which each good directive should possess. A good directive must encompass the formula of who, what, where, when, how, and why. The instruction should be accomplishable, intelligible, properly phrased, and compatible with the objectives of the enterprise. In addition to this a reasonable amount of time should be permitted.

In issuing directives the supervisor may employ two major techniques ranging all the way from the autocratic technique which brings about close supervision, to the participative, democratic, permissive kind of directing usually called consultative or general supervision. There are certain occasions, certain employees, and certain conditions under which the autocratic technique is probably the most effective one; but for most situations it is far better for a supervisor to apply consultative, participative techniques in order to produce the highest motivation and morale among the employees. This means that in case of new assignments the supervisor will consult with his employees as to how the job should best be done. He will elicit their contributions to a decision. In those directives which are primarily concerned with routine assignments and the daily performance of the job, the supervisor will employ a form of general supervision instead of close supervision. In so doing he gives his employees the freedom to make decisions themselves on how the job is to be done, after he has set the goals and standards which they are to achieve. It gives employees the freedom to use their own ingenuity and judgment, and situations of this type offer continuous ground for further training and improvement. In addition to this, it motivates the employees to the extent that they find satisfaction in their jobs. All indications are that general supervision produces better results than close supervision. Since the economic setting is of a dynamic nature necessitating changes, the supervisor is often confronted with the problem of how to introduce the necessary changes. In order to successfully cope with the average employee's normal resistance to change, the supervisor must know the reasons why this resistance exists, and what he can do to successfully cope with them.

15

MORALE

The supervisor's day-to-day function of direction and supervision is a very important factor in the morale of the employees. Although there are many different definitions for morale, it can be defined as a state of mind and emotion affecting the attitude and willingness to work, which in turn affects individual and organizational objectives. It is the attitude of individuals and groups toward their work, environment, management, and the enterprise. Morale is not a single feeling. It is a composite of feelings, sentiments, and attitudes, which, when it is good, makes people do what the organization expects them to do; and conversely, which, when it is low, prevents and deters the employees from doing what the organization expects them to do.

Supervisors often make the mistake of speaking of morale as something which is either present or absent among their employees. Morale is always present and by itself has neither favorable nor unfavorable meaning. Morale can range through a large number of degrees from excellent and positive to poor and completely negative. Morale by itself most certainly does not indicate the existence of a good state. If the attitude of the subordinates is very poor, then the morale is poor, and if the subordinates' state of mind and emotion affecting their willingness to work is high, then we speak of high morale. An employee with high morale is pleased with his position in the enterprise, has confidence in his and his associates' ability, shows enthusiasm and a strong desire for voluntary cooperation toward the hospital's objectives to the fullest extent of his ability.

High morale cannot be ordered. It can be created only by introducing certain conditions into the work situation which are favorable to its development. High morale is not the cause of good human relations. High morale is the result of good human relations. It is the result of good motivation, respect and dignity of the individual, realization of individual differences, good leadership, effective communication, participation, counseling, and many other human relations practices. The state of morale will reflect how appropriately and effectively the supervisor practices human relations.

MORALE—THE SUPERVISOR'S CONCERN   Every manager, from the top administrator down to the supervisor, should be concerned with the level of morale of the subordinates. A good supervisor is aware that it is his function to elicit and to maintain the morale of his subordinates at as high a level as possible. It is the immediate supervisor who, in his day-to-day contact with his employees, more than anyone else influences and determines the level of morale of his employees. Raising morale to a high level and maintaining it there is a long-run project and cannot be achieved with the help of short-run devices such as pep talks or contests. And the supervisor will find that athough good morale is slow to develop and difficult to maintain, it can change very quickly from good to bad with many shadings in between. The level of morale varies considerably from day to day and it is far more changeable than the weather. Morale is also contagious, and although favorable attitudes spread, it is true that unfavorable attitudes among employees spread even more quickly. It seems to be human nature to quickly forget the good and to remember the bad.

The supervisor is not alone in his desire for a satisfactory level of morale. Each employee of the institution is concerned with the state of morale since bad morale is not as satisfying to anyone as good morale. A state of bad morale does not make for good environment for the employees of the hospital and they have as much at stake as the administration. Good morale will make the employee's day at work a pleasure and not a misery. He will find satisfaction working with his supervisors and associates. High morale is also of importance to the patient in the hospital, who quickly senses whether or not the employees of the institution are operating on a high or a low level of morale.

The term morale defines the character of the total attitudes at a given time. The concept of morale pertains not only to an individual, but also to a group. Individual morale refers to the individual employees' attitudes whereas group morale is the general tone of the subordinates' attitude in the organization as a whole or in a particular department.

FACTORS INFLUENCING MORALE   Almost anything can influence the morale of the employees upward or downward. Some of these factors are within the control of the supervisor, whereas others are not. Although there are an infinite number of factors influencing morale, they can generally be classified into two broad groups: One broad group of factors has its primary source in situations which are external to the hospital, or related health facility; the other source lies mostly within the daily supervisory practices.

The first broad source of factors affecting morale, namely, those factors which are connected with events and influences outside the institution, are frequently beyond the scope of the supervisor. Although they are external in nature, they nevertheless significantly affect the morale of the employees at work. Examples of this source are family relations, association with friends, a breakdown of the car, sickness in the family, hobbies, and so forth. What has happened at home may change the employee's feeling very quickly; an argument before leaving for work may set the emotional tone for the rest of the day. The headlines in the morning paper may be depressing or they may be conducive to high morale.

This outside-of-the-hospital source of morale factors is beyond the supervisor's control, and can at best be dealt with only indirectly. Nevertheless, the supervisor should be alert to sense them because these incidents are reflected in the attitudes of the subordinate. If something has happened to lower the morale and if the supervisor is familiar with the cause, he should try to get the employee to forget the incident as quickly as possible by supplying an antidote. One of the best ways to erase the effects of an occurrence that depresses morale is to recognize the cause and to encourage the employee to talk about it freely. In so doing the supervisor will find out what is happening and why, and he may devise other effective means of action to raise morale. But, aside from this, there is little a supervisor can do to cope with these outside factors which affect the morale of his employees. The supervisor must remember that there are many influences at work to cause the level of the morale to shift continuously.

There is an important group of factors affecting the morale of employees which are all within the realm of the supervisor's activities. These are appropriate incentives, good working conditions, and above all, the quality of supervision. When considering incentives the first thing that comes to mind is pay. Of course wages are exceedingly important; but aside from wages and fringe benefits there are many other things which are essential to the employee. These are considerations such as job security, interesting work, good working conditions, appreciation of a job well done, and recognition. None of the latter will take the place of appropriate compensation in dollars and cents. But assuming that the pay is the going rate, the additional incentives mentioned above play a significant role. Although reasonable incentives are provided and the quality of supervision is high, morale can sink quickly if working conditions are neglected. The important factor is that an honest attempt is made to improve working conditions wherever possible. There are many examples where employees work under undesirable conditions and still maintain a high morale as long as the supervisor has made serious attempts to improve the conditions wherever possible.

Aside from these on-the-job factors influencing the morale of the employees, the most significant influence is exercised by the supervisor himself in his day-to-day immediate relationship with them. The boss's overall manner of supervision, directing, leadership, and general attitude will, more than anything else, make for good or bad morale. The employees will put forth their best efforts when they are given an opportunity to obtain their need satisfactions through work which they enjoy and at the same time help the organization. Job satisfaction which raises and keeps the morale at a high level can be increased by the supervisor by letting his employees know how significantly they contribute to the overall achievement of the hospital or related facility, how their work fits into the overall effort, by giving them a feeling of accomplishment in their work, and by allowing them to be their own boss as far as possible. In addition to this, the supervisor should not forget the importance of social satisfactions on the job by providing the employees with an opportunity to develop friendships and to work as a team. The supervisor who practices general supervision, as discussed in the previous chapter, is likely to reduce the undesirable features of a job and to create an environment in which his workers derive genuine satisfaction from the work they do every day, and in so doing contribute significantly to a high level of morale.

The supervisor should bear in mind that his employees' morale is affected not only by what he does, but also by the manner in which he acts. There is little doubt that if the supervisor's behavior indicates that he feels superior to his employees or that he is suspicious of their motives and actions, only a low level of morale can be the result. The supervisor should always bear in mind how little it takes to make his own spirits rise or fall. A word of appreciation from the hospital administrator can change the supervisor's outlook toward his whole work situation. He will become more cheerful and he will be in a happy mood. The supervisor also knows that a frown or a quizzical expression on the administrator's face can have the opposite effect. He will begin to wonder what he did wrong, his face will drop, and his morale will sink. The supervisor should remember that the employees of his department react the same way to him since he is their boss. He should remember that attitudes beget like attitudes. If the supervisor shows that he is worried, his employees tend to follow suit. If he loses his temper, others do the same and become angry. When the supervisor appears to be confident in the operation of the department, the employees will react accordingly and feel that things are going well. This does not mean that the supervisor should only see the good side of the operations and refuse to discover difficulties and troubles. What it means is that he should show his employees that as a leader of his department he has the situation well in hand, and that if something goes wrong, he will give them an opportunity to correct the situation and to see to it that it does not happen again in the future.

Obviously, the supervisor cannot ever relax in his efforts to build and maintain a high degree of morale among his employees. Nor should he be discouraged if, from time to time, the morale drops, since there are so many factors to cause this change which are beyond his control and out of the supervisor's reach. The supervisor can be reasonably satisfied when his employees' morale is high most of the time.

MORALE AND TEAMWORK   The term teamwork is often associated with morale. However, the two do not mean the same. Morale applies to the attitudes of the employees of the department, whereas teamwork is the smoothly coordinated and synchronized activity achieved by a closely knit small group of employees. Although good morale is helpful in achieving teamwork, it is possible that teamwork may be high yet morale low. Such a situation could exist in times when jobs are scarce and when the employees will put up with close and tight supervision for fear of losing their jobs. And then again, it is conceivable that teamwork may be absent when morale is high; in such a case the employee prefers individual effort and finds satisfaction in his own performance.

MORALE AND PRODUCTIVITY   It is generally assumed that high morale is automatically accompanied by high productivity. Supervisors feel that as long as the morale of the employees is high the output will be accordingly high. Every supervisor knows that the willing cooperation of the employees is necessary to get continuous superior production. Much research has been done in this area. Although there are many ramifications to such a general statement, there is substantial evidence that employees produce best under the supervisor who keeps the morale high. Every supervisor knows from his own experience that a highly motivated, self-disciplined group of employees will consistently do a more satisfactory job than one which is forced to do so. It is, therefore, obvious that every supervisor will do all in his power to keep the level of morale as high as possible in order to keep the output in his department at a high level. Aside from the fact that high morale has a close relationship to high productivity, the supervisor is interested in maintaining a high level of morale also simply for the fact that it makes the work pleasant for all the members of the department. A generally pleasant attitude throughout is bound to make for better productivity.

MEASURING CURRENT MORALE   Morale cannot be measured directly. But there are suitable ways and means which will describe and indicate the prevailing level of morale and its trends. Although some supervisors pride themselves on their ability to intuitively detect low morale, the wise supervisor will do better to approach this problem more systematically. One approach is through observation of activities, events, trends, and changes, and the other approach is to use what is commonly referred to as attitude surveys.

Measuring current morale by observation Observation is the simple tool of watching for personal manifestations, and although it is available to every supervisor, it is not often utilized fully. If the supervisor consciously and systematically observes his employees he can appraise the level of morale and any changes. He watches the subordinates' behavior, listens to what they have to say; he will observe their actions and notice any changes in willingness to cooperate. It is not difficult to recognize by observation the extremes of high and low morale. Finer means of measurement, however, are required to differentiate among the intermediate degrees. There will be personal manifestations of the employee such as a facial expression or a shrug of the shoulder which reflect the true level of morale. Admittedly it is very difficult to describe how far from normal the behavior must be in order to indicate a change in morale. It takes a sensitive supervisor to conclude from indicators of this sort that a change in morale has taken or is taking place.

The closeness of the day-to-day working relationships usually offers much opportunity for the supervisor to become aware of these changes. However, it often happens that supervisors are so burdened with work that they do not have the time to look or, if they look, they actually do not see. At times they may even be afraid to look for fear of what they might find. Although supervisors may realize changes are there, most of the time they do not think much about them and are inclined to ignore them without giving the matter further attention and thought. Only later, after the change in the level of morale has taken place to such a degree that it has openly manifested itself, will the supervisor recall these first indications, and only then will he admit that he had noticed them, but had not thought much about them at the time.

The supervisor is in an excellent position to measure the morale of his subordinates by his day-to-day observation. He must sharpen his powers of observation, and he must take care not to brush any indicators conveniently aside. The serious shortcoming of observation as a yardstick to measure current morale is that the activities and events indicate a change to a lowered morale which has already occurred. The supervisor, therefore, should be extremely keen in his observation in order to do as much as possible to prevent such changes and to speedily counteract them. He should be alert to sense them as they are reflected in the attitude of the employees, and the closer the supervisor's relations are with his employees the more sensitive will he become to these changes.

Morale or attitude surveys Many institutions use morale or attitude surveys as a way of finding out how the employees feel about their jobs, their supervisors, the hospital as a whole, specific policies, and so on. Expressions of opinions of the employees are requested in the form of answers to written questionnaires. These questionnaires are prepared with the aid of the personnel department or some outside consulting firm, and they may be filled out on the job or at home. Although there are many advantages in filling out these questionnaires in the privacy of the home, it is to be expected that a high percentage of those questionnaires which are sent home are never returned. Of course, regardless of whether they are filled out on the job or at home, care must be taken that they remain unsigned and that the replies will be kept secret.

Questionnaires submitted to the employees come in a variety of types. Some questionnaires offer a choice of answering the questions from a specific list of answers; others are not so specific, giving the employee the opportunity to answer as freely as he would like to. Since many employees have difficulty in stating their opinions in complete sentences or by merely completing a started sentence, the best results are usually obtained by a form where the employee checks a box which seems to be the most appropriate answer for him.

Once the forms have been filled out the results must be tabulated and analyzed. This is usually done by the personnel department, and the results are presented to the top administrator who, in turn, passes them on to all supervisors. As a matter of fact, in some organizations these morale surveys are used as discussion material in supervisory training. But aside from this side effect, the attitude surveys provide the administrator with an instrument and information to guide the administration in the effort to improve morale if deficiencies exist. Occasionally the surveys will reveal certain deficiencies, and the supervisor can do something very specific about them in order to eliminate the misunderstanding. But very frequently the results of surveys are not so clear. They raise a lot of questions, and a careful study must be made as to the hospital's policies and other aspects in order to arrive at the solution.

It is necessary that management implement the results of a survey if a survey has been made. It would be demoralizing for the employees if a survey has been made and if the administration does nothing in order to correct the dissatisfactions which have been expressed. If the administration does not intend to implement the survey it would be far better not to take one. No doubt these surveys are time-consuming and expensive. But since it is significant for the supervisor to maintain as high a level of morale as possible, it is well worth making one. In all of this, of course, the supervisor must receive guidance and assistance from the personnel department.

SUMMARY   Morale is a state of mind and emotions affecting the attitude and willingness to work. It is the attitude of individuals and groups toward their work environment, supervision and the enterprise as a whole. It is a composite and not a single feeling. Morale is always present, and it can range all the way from high morale to low morale. The level of morale varies considerably from day to day. It is contagious; favorable attitudes spread, but unfavorable attitudes spread even more quickly. High morale is not only the concern of the supervisor—the employees are just as interested in a satisfactory level of morale. Not only do the insiders feel the effect of a high or low level of morale, it is just as recognizable to the outsiders coming in contact with the enterprise.

Morale and teamwork are not synonymous. The general statement that high morale will bring with it increased productivity is proven by every supervisor's common daily experience. However, recent research indicates that there may be other ramifications to this general statement.

Morale can be influenced by a multitude of factors which consist of primarily two broad groups, namely those factors affecting the employee's activities outside of the enterprise and those factors pertaining to on-the-job situations. There is relatively little the boss can do to change the effects of the outside factors on his subordinates' morale, but there is much within his power to raise the morale of his employees to a high level with the aid of good supervision. The supervisor's day-to-day direct supervision of the employees will significantly influence the level of the subordinates' morale.

An astute supervisor can sense the change of the level in morale by merely observing his subordinates. But a keen sense of observation is necessary to notice a change in the level of morale, and often supervisors do not realize that a change has taken place until it is late. Another means of becoming familiar with the level of morale is to perform a morale or attitude survey with the help of the personnel department. This is primarily done by questionnaires submitted to the employees. Once a morale survey has been performed, it is absolutely necessary that management do something about those points which have been brought to light as contributing to the lowering of morale. In conclusion, good supervision as advocated in this text can raise low morale to high morale.

16

DISCIPLINE

Discipline is another concept which is intrinsically related to the managerial function of supervising. The word discipline is used in many connections and understood in several different ways. When one hears the word discipline, one is inclined to think immediately of the use of authority or force. To many it primarily carries the disagreeable connotation of the need for punishment. However, there is another way of considering the matter of discipline, a way which is far more in keeping with what has been said about good supervision. For our purposes discipline can be thought of as a state of affairs—of a condition in an enterprise in which there is orderliness, in which the members of the enterprise behave themselves sensibly and conduct themselves according to the standards of acceptable behavior as expressed by the needs of the organization. Discipline is said to be good when the employees willingly practice self-discipline, willingly follow the rules of the enterprise. Discipline is said to be bad when subordinates either do this reluctantly or actually disobey regulations and the standards of acceptable behavior.

DISCIPLINE AND MORALE Discipline is not the same as morale. Morale, as discussed before, is an attitude, a state of mind, whereas discipline is a state of affairs. But the level of morale significantly influences the problems of discipline. Normally it can be expected that there will be fewer problems of discipline whenever the morale is high. By the same token low morale brings about more problems of discipline. However, it is also conceivable that there could be a high degree of discipline in spite of a low level of morale. Under those conditions discipline probably is controlled by fear and sheer force. Then again, it is usually not possible to maintain a high level of morale unless there is a high degree of discipline.

SELF-DISCIPLINE   The best discipline is self-discipline. This is the normal human tendency to do what needs to be done and to do one's share, to do the right thing, and to subordinate some of one's own needs and desires to the standards of acceptable behavior set for the enterprise. Experience shows that most employees want to do the right thing. Even before they start to work most mature persons accept the idea that following instructions and fair rules of conduct is a normal responsibility which goes with any job. Most employees can be counted on to exercise a considerable degree of self-discipline. They believe in doing things the right way, in coming to work on time, following the supervisor's instructions, punching the time clock, refraining from fights, drinking at work or stealing, and so on. Self-imposed discipline involves conformity with the rules, regulations, and orders which are necessary for the proper conduct of the enterprise. This conformity calls for a reasonable degree of subordination of personal interests to the needs of the enterprise.

Once the employees know what is expected of them and feel that the rules by which they are governed are reasonable, they usually will observe them without problems. When new rules are introduced the supervisor must make it his business to show their reasonableness and need to the employees. The strong sense of self-imposed discipline on the employees' part will exert group pressure on any possible wrongdoer, thus reducing the need for disciplinary action. The employee knows that he will have the unqualified support of his supervisor as long as he stays within the ordinary rules of conduct and as long as his activities are consistent with what is expected of him. Proper discipline makes it necessary to give positive support to the right action, but to also criticize and punish the wrong action. The subordinate must know that failure to live up to what is expected of him will result in "punishment."

Administration cannot expect the employees to practice self-discipline unless self-imposed discipline starts at the top. There are similar restrictions imposed upon all managerial personnel to remain within the acceptable patterns of behavior. Supervisors cannot expect their workers to impose self-discipline if the supervisors themselves do not show it. Such proper conduct with respect to the needs of the organization requires the supervisor

214

to comply with the necessity to be on time, to observe "no smoking" and "no drinking" rules, to dress and to behave in a socially approved manner commensurate with his activities.

DISCIPLINARY ACTION

Although the vast majority of employees will exercise a considerable degree of self-discipline, unfortunately there are a few employees in every large organization who, for some reason or other, occasionally fail to observe established rules and standards even after having been informed of them. There are some employees who simply will not accept the responsibility of self-discipline. Since the job must go on, the supervisor cannot afford to let those few "get away with" violations. Assuming that the supervisor has done his best, firm action is called for to correct the situation. Unless such action is taken the morale of the other employees in the work group would be seriously weakened. This is the time when the supervisor has to refer to the authority inherent in his position even though he may dislike doing so. On this occasion the supervisor must clearly realize the fact that he is in charge of the department, that he is responsible for discipline within it. If the supervisor does not take appropriate action it may encourage some individuals who are merely on the borderline of being undisciplined to become encouraged to follow the bad example. When a defect in discipline becomes apparent, it is the supervisor's responsibility to take proper action firmly and, of course, wisely.

TAKING ACTION[1]   Normally, a good supervisor will not have too much occasion to take disciplinary action. But whenever it becomes necessary it is the supervisor's job to do so. This undoubtedly is an unpleasant task. But it is an inescapable part of supervision. In his supervisory capacity, the supervisor is best qualified to know the employee, the conditions, and the circumstances. Since he is the manager in charge of his department, he has the authority and responsibility to take appropriate ac-

[1]In all of our discussions it is assumed that the employees of the department do not belong to a union, and therefore no contractual obligations restrict the supervisor's authority in the realm of disciplinary action.

tion. Although it may be expedient for the moment to let the personnel director handle unpleasant problems of this type, the supervisor would be shirking his responsibility and he would be abdicating and undermining his own position.

The supervisor cannot afford to ignore or to conveniently overlook a subordinate's failure to meet the prescribed standards of conduct. If the supervisor condones such breaches he is merely communicating to the rest of the employees the fact that he does not intend to enforce the rules and regulations. On the other hand, the supervisor must caution himself against haste or unwarranted action. Before he does anything it is necessary for the supervisor to investigate what happened and why. He also should check the employee's past record and all other pertinent information he can easily obtain before he takes any action.

Whenever taking disciplinary action the supervisor must continuously caution himself not to lose his temper. Regardless of the severity of the violation the supervisor must not permit himself to lose control of the situation by losing his temper and thus run the risk of losing the respect of all of his employees. This does not mean that he should face the situation half-heartedly or haphazardly. If the supervisor should feel that he is in danger of losing control of his emotions he should, by all means, avoid action until he has cooled down. Even if the violation is significant, the supervisor cannot afford to lose control of the situation or control of his emotions. By the same token, the supervisor should follow the general rule of never laying a hand on an employee in any way. Except for emergencies where an employee has been injured or becomes ill, or where he needs to separate employees who are fighting, such a gesture could easily be misunderstood.

PRIVACY   The supervisor must make certain that all disciplinary action takes place between the supervisor and the employee involved as a private matter. It most certainly should never be done in public. A public reprimand builds up resentment in the employee being reprimanded. In addition to this, other factors enter the situation if the supervisor tries to reprimand an employee in public. For instance, if in the opinion of the other workers, a disciplinary action is too severe for the violation, the disciplined employee would appear as a martyr to the rest of them. If the supervisor is disciplining in public he is bound to have his performance judged by every other employee in the department. In addition to this, it is possible that the employees may not agree with the facts on which the supervisor is basing his disciplinary action. Before he knows it he will be arguing with all the other employees, and it is a well known fact that eyewitness reports vary extensively. In addition to this, of course, it would humiliate the disciplined employee in the eyes of his co-workers and cause considerable damage to the entire department. Therefore, privacy in taking disciplinary action must be the rule.

TYPES OF DISCIPLINARY ACTION The question of the type of disciplinary action is answered differently in different enterprises. But in recent years many enterprises have accepted the idea of a progressive discipline which provides for an increase in the penalty with each "offense." Unless a serious wrong has been committed, the employee is rarely discharged for the first offense. The following list of the various steps of disciplinary action is merely suggested, and it should not be construed to mean that these are the only means of disciplinary action or necessarily in their proper order. But many companies have found these steps to be quite workable: 1) informal talk; 2) oral warning or reprimand; 3) written or official warning; 4) disciplinary layoff; 5) demotional downgrading or transfer; 6) discharge.

1. *The informal talk* If the incident is of a minor nature and the employee is one whose record has no marks of disciplinary action, an informal, friendly talk will clear up the situation in many cases. In such a talk the supervisor will discuss with the employee the behavior in relation to the standards which prevail within the enterprise. During this interview the supervisor will try to get to the underlying reason for this undesirable behavior. At the same time he will try to reaffirm the employee's sense of responsibility and to reestablish his previous cooperative relationship within the department. Of course, in such a friendly, informal talk it is necessary that the supervisor does not lose his temper or become abusive. In many instances this informal talk will take care of minor violations. It may be advisable to repeat once more why the action of the employee is undesirable

217

and what it possibly may lead to. If this friendly talk is not sufficient to bring about the desired results then it will become necessary for the supervisor to take the next step, namely that of an oral warning.

2. *Oral warning or reprimand* In this interview between the employee and the supervisor it should again be pointed out how undesirable the subordinate's violation is and that it ultimately could lead to some disciplinary action. The violation should be discussed in a straightforward statement of fact and the supervisor should not begin with a recital of how the fine reputation of the employee has now been "tarnished." The supervisor should stress the preventive purpose of discipline by his manner and words but, nevertheless, he must put the employee on notice that such conduct cannot be tolerated. At the same time he will emphasize the fact that unless the employee improves he will be subject to further official disciplinary action. In some enterprises there is a record made on the employee's papers that this oral warning has taken place, whereas in others such record may not be written. Of course, the oral warning's purpose is to help the employee to correct his behavior and to prevent the need for further disciplinary action. It should leave the employee with the feeling that he is confident that he can do better and will improve in the future. Some supervisors feel that oral reprimand is not very effective. However, if this is carried out skillfully, many employees will be straigthened out at this stage.

3. *Written or official warning* Written warning is of a formal nature insofar as it becomes a part of the employee's record. Written warnings are particularly necessary in unionized concerns so that the document can serve as evidence in case of grievance procedures. The written warning, of which the employee receives a duplicate, must contain a statement of the violation and the potential consequences. A duplicate of this warning is sent to the personnel department so that it can be inserted in the permanent record.

4. *Disciplinary layoffs* This penalty would be next in line in case the employee has performed repeated and continued offenses and where all previous steps were of no avail. Under such conditions the supervisor must determine which penalty would be appropriate. This, of course, will depend on how serious the of-

fense has been and whether this action is the first, second, or third offense, or even more than that. Usually, disciplinary layoffs extend over several days or weeks. Seldom are they ever more than a few weeks. Some employees may not be very impressed with oral or written warnings but will find a disciplinary layoff without pay a rude awakening and will be convinced that the enterprise is really serious. A disciplinary layoff may bring back a sense of compliance with rules and regulations. There are, of course, a number of disadvantages to invoking disciplinary layoff, and therefore some enterprises do not apply this disciplinary measure. They reason that they are hurting their own production by laying off one of their trained employees, especially in times of labor shortages, when they will not be able to replace him with someone who is just as skilled. It is also felt that the employee will return from his layoff even in a much more unpleasant frame of mind than when he left. Therefore, quite a few companies are not any longer employing the measure of disciplinary layoff.

5. Demotional downgrading This is another disciplinary measure the usefulness of which is seriously questioned. To demote for disciplinary reasons to a less paying job is likely to bring about dissatisfaction and discouragement. As a matter of fact, to lose pay over an extended period of time is a form of constant punishment. Such dissatisfaction may easily spread to others in his new group. Therefore, many enterprises may avoid downgrading as a disciplinary measure just as they do disciplinary layoff. If so, they will have to use termination of employment as the ultimate penalty in serious cases.

6. Discharge Discharge is the most drastic form of disciplinary action, and it should be reserved only for the most serious offenses. Due to the serious implications of discharge supervisors will resort to it less and less frequently. Discharge eliminates all seniority standing an employee may have had, and makes it difficult for him to obtain new employment. As far as the enterprise is concerned, discharges involve serious losses and waste, including the expense of training a new employee and the expense of the disruption caused by changing the makeup of the work team. There may also be damage to the morale of the group.

Because of the serious implications and consequences of discharge, some enterprises, especially in unionized concerns, have reserved this right to discharge an employee for higher management and have taken it away from the supervisor. In addition to the severe economic consequences and cost of discharge, management in unionized companies is concerned with possible prolonged arbitration procedures, knowing full well that arbitrators have become increasingly unwilling to permit discharge except for the most severe cases of violations. Of course, there may be cases where there is no other answer but to fire the employee for "just cause." These cases will be the exception and not the rule.

TIME ELEMENT   In all of these disciplinary steps the time element is of significance. The question arises of how long the breaking of a rule should be held against an employee. Current practice is inclined to disregard offenses which have been committed more than a year or two years previous. Therefore, an employee with a poor record on account of tardiness would start a new life if he maintained a good record for one year. This time element, of course, will also vary, depending on the nature of the violation. If an employee should be brandishing a loaded gun in a heated argument during work there is no need to worry about any time element or previous offenses. This is enough to warrant immediate discharge.

PURPOSE OF DISCIPLINE

All of this disciplinary action must be undertaken with sensitivity and wisdom on the supervisor's part. It is meaningless to discipline a subordinate merely in the spirit of retribution or to humiliate him. Discipline is not for the purpose of "getting even" with the employee. Disciplinary action must have as its goal the improvement of the future behavior of the subordinate and the other members of the organization. The purpose and the meaning of the supervisor's action must be the avoidance of a similar occurrence in the future.

THE SUPERVISOR'S QUANDARY   In spite of all the sensitivity and wisdom with which the supervisor takes disciplinary action, it puts the supervisor in a difficult position. It is very difficult to impose discipline without generating resentment because disciplinary action is by nature an unpleasant experience. The question therefore arises of how the supervisor can apply the necessary disciplinary action so that it will be the least resented. In this connection Douglas McGregor refers to what he calls the "hot stove rule" and draws a comparison between touching a hot stove and experiencing discipline. When one touches a hot stove the discipline is immediate, with warning, consistent, and impersonal. First, the burn was immediate, and there was no question of the cause and effect. Second, there was a warning. Everyone knows what happens if one touches a stove, especially when the stove is red hot. Third, the discipline was consistent. Every time one touches a stove one is burned. Fourth, the discipline is impersonal. Whoever touches the stove is burned; it does not matter who he is. He is burned because of what he does, because he touched the stove, not because of who he is. The comparison illustrates the fact that the act and the discipline is almost one. The discipline takes place because the person did something, because he committed a particular act. The discipline is directed against the act and not against the person. Following these four basic rules will help the supervisor take the sting out of many disciplinary actions.

IMMEDIATE   A prompt beginning of the disciplinary process is necessary as soon as possible after the supervisor notices the violation. The sooner the discipline is invoked, the more automatic it will seem to be and the closer the connection with the offensive act. Of course, the supervisor should refrain from taking hasty action, and enough time should elapse for tempers to cool and for the assembling of all the necessary facts. Immediacy means that once the supervisor has noticed the offense, he goes about taking disciplinary action as speedily as possible. But he must caution himself not to make such haste as to run the danger of taking unwarranted action.

Temporary suspension   There are instances where it is apparent that the employee is guilty of a violation although the full circumstances may not be known. There are cases where the need for disciplinary action is unquestionable but there is doubt as to the amount of penalty. There are other times when the nature of the incident makes it necessary to get the offender off the premises quickly. Some immediate action seems necessary. To solve this dilemma many enterprises invoke what is called "temporary suspension"; the employee is suspended pending final decision in the case. This device of suspension protects management and the employee. It gives management the chance to make the necessary investigation and an opportunity for tempers to cool off. In case of temporary suspension the employee is told that he is "suspended" and that he will be informed as soon as possible as to the disciplinary action that will be taken. Suspension, in itself, is not a punishment. If the investigation shows that there is no cause for disciplinary action, the employee has no grievance case since he is recalled and he will not have suffered any loss of pay. If, on the other hand, a penalty should be applied and if this should be a disciplinary layoff, then the time during which he was suspended will constitute part of whatever disciplinary layoff has been assessed. The obvious advantage of this device of suspension is that the supervisor can act promptly without any prejudice to the employee. But in spite of the fact that temporary suspension is an advantageous and convenient method of disciplinary action, it should not be used indiscriminately.

ADVANCE WARNING   In order to have good discipline and to have the employees accept disciplinary action as fair, it is absolutely essential that all employees must be clearly informed in advance as to what is expected of them. The employees must have been informed clearly as to what the plant rules are. There must be warning that a certain offense will lead to disciplinary action, and there must be a clear warning as to the various degrees of disciplinary action which will normally be invoked. It is the supervisor's obligation to make certain that the employees know what the rules are and how they are to be enforced. Some enterprises refer to bulletin board announcements. But these cannot be as effective as a section in an employee handbook which every new employee receives whenever he starts working for the institution. In addition to the written statements it is advisable to include further clarification of these rules in the handbook. During the induction process shortly after a new employee is hired, he should be orally informed regarding the enterprise and what is expected of him.

In addition to the forewarning about rules, it is essential to let the employees know in advance about the kind of disciplinary action that will be taken. It is necessary to clarify to the employees the kind of disciplinary action to which they would become subject before they could possibly become involved in an offense. There are considerable doubts as to whether or not a standard penalty should be provided for and stated for each offense. In other words, should there be a clear statement, for instance, that falsifying production records will carry a one week disciplinary layoff? Those in favor of a list suggest that it would be an effective warning and that it would provide greater consistency. There are those who do not believe in posting such a list of prescribed penalties for the reason that this would not permit management to take into consideration the various degrees of guilt and the circumstances. It probably is best not to provide such a list with standard penalties for specific violations, but merely to state the various steps of disciplinary action which will be taken in an orderly sequence. It should be stated that continued violations will bring more severe penalties. There are some enterprises which specify that certain offenses such as drinking liquor on the premises, or fighting, will bring the penalty of immediate discharge. But, generally speaking, it is unwise to spell out a rigid set of disciplinary measures for a specific violation.

It is very likely that in every enterprise there are certain rules which have been posted and also printed in the employees' handbooks but which have never been enforced. Since the supervisor has never disciplined anyone who violated them, the employees do not expect these rules to be enforced in the future. Suddenly the supervisor may decide that in order to make a rule valid he is going to make "an example of one of the employees" and takes disciplinary action. Of course, this he should not do in this manner. The fact that a certain rule has not been enforced in the past does not mean that it cannot ever be enforced. What it does mean is that the supervisor must take certain steps before he can begin to enforce this rule. Instead of acting tough suddenly, he should give his employees some warning that this rule, enforcement of which has been lax, will be strictly enforced in the future. In such cases it is not enough to put the notice on the bulletin board. It is essential that in addition to a clear, written warning supplemental oral communication be given. It is absolutely necessary to familiarize the workers with the fact that from the present time on the supervisor intends to enforce this rule. It is his job to put them on notice in this respect, and just posting it on the blackboard is not sufficient.

BE CONSISTENT   A further requirement of good discipline makes it necessary for the supervisor to be consistent. The supervisor must be consistent in the enforcement of discipline, and he must be consistent in the disciplinary action he takes. To be inconsistent is one of the fastest ways for a supervisor to lower the morale of his employees and to lose their respect. By being consistent the supervisor sets the limit for acceptable behavior, and every individual wants to know what the limits are. If the employee does not know what the rules are, if the supervisor is inconsistent, then the employee finds himself in an environment in which he cannot feel secure. Inconsistency will only lead to insecurity and anxiety, and create doubts in the employee's mind as to what he can do and what he cannot do. At times the supervisor may feel inclined to be lenient and to overlook an infringement. In reality, he is not doing the employee any favor. He is only making it harder for him and the others.

Mason Haire, a well known psychologist, compares this situation with the relations between a motorist and a traffic policeman. Whenever we are exceeding the speed limit on the highway we must feel some sort of anxiety since we are breaking the rule. On the other hand, the rule is often not enforced. We think that perhaps this is a place where the police department does not take the rule seriously and we can speed a little. But there is always the lurking insecurity because the motorist knows that at any time the policeman decides to enforce the rule he can do so. Most motorists from time to time feel that it would be easier to operate in a situation where the policeman would be at least consistent either one way or the other. The same situation holds true for the employees in the case where the supervisor is not consistent in his disciplinary activities.

The employees are eager to be treated fairly by the supervisor, and exercising consistent discipline is one way to demonstrate the supervisor's sense of fair play. But this is often difficult for the supervisor to do. There are times when the department is particularly rushed with a large amount of work, and the supervisor may be induced to overlook infringements because he does not want to upset the work force or he is afraid that if he has to suspend someone he will lose a valuable employee at a critical time. The same kind of consideration may hold true when it is difficult to get an employee with a certain skill, and the offending employee possesses that skill.

In addition to all this, the supervisor is in a difficult position. On the one hand he has been continuously cautioned to treat all of his employees alike and to avoid favoritism, and on the other hand he has been told again and again to treat people as individuals in accordance with their special needs and situations. On the surface these two requirements contradict each other, and to apply consistent discipline seems to be impossible. The supervisor can never forget that each employee has special needs and that each situation must be considered by itself. On the other hand, he realizes that what may appear to be inconsistent discipline would create bad feelings among the other employees.

Treating people fairly does not mean treating everyone exactly in the same manner. What it means is that when an exception is made it must be accepted as a valid exception by the other members of the department. The rest of the employees will accept an exception as fair if it is known why it was made and if it is considered as justified. In addition to this, the rest of the employees must be confident that if any other employee were in the same situation he would receive the same treatment. If these conditions are fulfilled, the supervisor has been able to exercise fair play, be consistent in his discipline, and still treat people as individuals.

The extent to which a supervisor can be consistent and yet consider the individual situation is illustrated as follows. Assume that three employees were engaged in some kind of horseplay. It could very well be that the supervisor will have merely a friendly, informal talk with one of the employees since he just started work a few days ago. The second employee may receive a formal or written warning since he has been warned about horseplay before. And it is conceivable that the third employee would receive a two or three day disciplinary layoff since he has been involved in many previous cases of horseplay. Each case must be considered on its own merit and each employee must be judged according to his background, personal history, length of service, and other factors of this type. Of course, if two of the employees had been in the same situation with the same amount of previous warnings then their penalty would have to be identical. In this respect consistency must prevail.

BE IMPERSONAL   It is only natural that an employee will feel resentment toward a supervisor if the latter has taken disciplinary action against him. The only way the supervisor can reduce the amount of resentment is to take disciplinary action on as impersonal a basis as possible. In recalling the hot stove rule, it is worth remembering that whoever touches the stove is burned regardless of who he is. He was burned not because of who he is but simply because he touched the stove. This is the kind of thinking and reasoning which can take the personal element out of disciplinary action and which is likely to reduce resentment. The penalty is connected with the act and not the person, and looking at disciplinary action this way minimizes any danger to the personal relationship between the supervisor and the employee. It is the act which brings about the disciplinary action, not the personality.

It is therefore advisable for the supervisor to discuss the happening in an objective manner, excluding the personal element as far as possible. Once a disciplinary action has been taken, the supervisor must let bygones be bygones. The supervisor must treat the employee as he always has treated him before and he must forget about what has happened. This is easier said than done. Only the mature person can handle discipline without feeling hostility or guilt. Not only is disciplinary action distasteful to the employee, it is probably just as distasteful to the supervisor who metes it out. The supervisor should take disciplinary action without being apologetic about what he has to do and without a sign of anger. By trying to observe these requirements he will make disciplinary action impersonal and in so doing it will be easier for the employee to get over it and for the supervisor to impose it.

CHANCE OF APPEAL   Everyone is familiar with the various steps of the grievance procedure to which each employee has access if he belongs to a union. But this right of appeal should exist in the same manner in an enterprise which does not have a union. It must be possible for the employee to appeal the supervisor's decision in reference to disciplinary action. Following the chain of command, the immediate supervisor's boss would be the one to whom such an appeal should be directed. Many companies have provided for such a procedure. But great care must be taken that this right of appeal is a real right and not merely a formality. There are supervisors who will gladly tell their subordinates that they can go to the next higher boss, but they will never forgive them if they do. Statements and thinking of this type merely indicate the supervisor's own insecurity in his managerial position. As a superior he must permit the employee to take this appeal to his boss without any resentment. It is management's obligation to provide such an appeal procedure, and the supervisor must not feel slighted in his role as a manager or as a leader of his department. It is very likely that management's failure to provide such appeal procedure is one of the chief reasons why employees take recourse to unionization. Such an appeal procedure is badly needed, and if the line managers do not provide it there is a likelihood that the employees will enlist the aid of a union to do this.

There is no doubt that it takes a mature supervisor not to see a threat in his position from such appeal procedure. Such a situation should be handled very tactfully by the supervisor's boss. It is possible that in the course of an appeal the disciplinary penalty imposed by the supervisor may be reduced or completely removed. It is understandable that under these circumstances the supervisor may become discouraged since his boss has not backed him up. Although this is unfortunate it is preferable that in a few instances a guilty employee may go free instead of an innocent employee being punished. It often happens that the reason for the reversal of the decision is that the supervisor has been inconsistent in his exercise of discipline or that he may not have obtained all the necessary facts before he imposed a disciplinary action. In order to avoid such an unpleasant situation it is necessary for the supervisor to adhere closely to all that has been said in this chapter before taking disciplinary action. If a supervisor is a wise disciplinarian he will normally find his verdict upheld by his boss. And if it should be reversed, this is still not too high a price to pay in order to give every employee the right to appeal.

SUMMARY Discipline is a state of affairs. It is likely that if morale is high discipline will be good and less need will exist for the supervisor to take disciplinary action. A supervisor is entitled to assume that most of his employees want to do the right thing and that much of the discipline is self-imposed—imposed upon themselves by the employees. Nevertheless, if the occasion should arise, it is essential for the supervisor to take disciplinary action. There usually is a progressive list of disciplinary actions leading all the way from informal talk and an oral warning, to "capital punishment," namely discharge. The supervisor should bear in mind that the purpose of discipline is not retribution or humiliation of employees. The goal of disciplinary action is the improvement of the future behavior of the subordinate in question and the other members of the organization. The purpose and meaning is to avoid similar occurrences in the future. Taking disciplinary action is a painful experience not only for the employee but also for the supervisor. In order to do the best possible job the supervisor must bear in mind that all disciplinary action must fulfill as much as possible the requirements of immediacy, forewarning, and consistency, and it must be impersonal in nature. In a well-run enterprise it is necessary that the chance of appeal must exist for an employee even in nonunionized enterprises.

PART VI

CONTROLLING

17

CONTROL: REQUIREMENTS, BASIC STEPS AND BUDGETS

Control is the process of checking to determine whether or not plans are being adhered to, whether or not proper progress is being made toward the objective, and acting, if necessary, to correct any deviations. The essence of control is action which adjusts performance to predetermined standards, if deviations from these standards occur. Control is one of the five managerial functions. The supervisor is responsible for results which in this connection means operational conformance to standards. The supervisor must make certain that all functions within his department adhere to the established standards, and, if not, that corrective action is taken. At times the manager may enlist the aid of experts within the organization only for assistance in obtaining information and data and counsel. But it would be out of order for the supervisor to expect anyone else to perform the controlling function for him.

Planning, organizing, staffing, and directing are the preparatory steps for getting the work done. Controlling is concerned with making certain that the execution is properly implemented. Without controlling, the supervisor is not doing a complete job of managing. Control remains necessary whenever a supervisor assigns duties to a subordinate. It is necessary for the supervisor to control because he has not shifted his responsibility.

Control is checking to ascertain whether or not plans are observed, suitable progress toward the objective made, and whether or not the directive is executed as intended. Control also includes, if necessary, correcting any deviations.

The eventual success of a department depends on the degree of difference between what should be done and what is done. Having set up the standards of performance, the supervisor must keep himself informed of the actual performance through observation, reports, discussion, and control charts. It is the supervisor's job to evaluate the difference between what should be done and what is accomplished. The supervisor must determine the difference and must prescribe the corrections necessary to bring about full compliance between the standards and the actual performance.

Although control is usually treated as a separate function, it is actually a part of the total managerial process of the supervisor. The line between control and the other managerial functions is not sharp. As a matter of fact, it is advisable to look at control within the circular movement of all managerial functions. In the managerial process of planning, the supervisor sets the goals, and these goals become standards against which performance is checked and appraised. There is a direct connection between planning and controlling. If there are deviations between the achievements and the standards, the supervisor will have to take corrective action and this corrective action itself may entail new plans and new standards. This illustrates the close relation between planning and controlling.

It also should be kept in mind that control is directly interwoven with all other managerial functions. Effective controlling affects them and controlling is affected by the other functions as well. A supervisor cannot expect to have good control over his department unless he follows sound managerial principles in pursuing his duties. Well made plans, workable policies and procedures, continuous training of his employees, good instructions, and good supervision all play a significant role in the results. Of course, the better these requirements are fulfilled, the easier will be the supervisor's function of controlling and the less the need for taking corrective action.

CONTROL IS FORWARD-LOOKING   There is nothing the supervisor can do about the past. If, for instance, the work assigned to a subordinate for the day has not been accomplished, the controlling process cannot correct the past. There are some supervisors who are inclined to scold at the person responsible and assume that he was negligent and deliberate when something goes wrong. There is no use "crying over spilled milk." The wise supervisor will look forward rather than backward. However, the supervisor must study the past in order to learn what has taken place and why it happened. He can learn from the past, and he should take proper steps to assure corrective action for the future. Since control is forward-looking, it is essential that deviations from the established standards are discovered by the supervisor as quickly as possible. Therefore, it is the supervisor's duty to minimize the time lag between results and corrective action. For example, instead of waiting until the day is over, it probably would be advisable for the supervisor to check at mid-day whether or not the job is progressing satisfactorily. But even then that particular morning is already in the past and nothing can be done about that any longer. Although this is a painful thought to a supervisor, he cannot alter the fact that effective control takes place after the event has occurred. This is often unavoidable. But minimizing the time lag between results and doing something about them will enable the supervisor to take prompt corrective action before the damage has gone too far.

Knowing how far to follow up is a real test of any supervisor's talents. The closeness of follow-up is based on many factors, such as the experience, initiative, dependability, resourcefulness of the employee who is given the assignment. Giving an employee an assignment and allowing him to do the job is the real test of delegation. This does not mean that the supervisor should leave him completely alone until it is time to inspect the final results. Nor does it mean that he should be "breathing down his subordinate's neck" and watching every detail. The supervisor must be familiar with the ability of his subordinate in order to determine how much leeway he can give him, how close he has to follow through.

REQUIREMENTS OF A CONTROL SYSTEM

Before discussing the essential steps in controlling, it is advisable to point out the basic requirements of a workable control system. For such a system to work it is necessary that controls be understandable, that they register deviations quickly and are timely, that the system provides for appropriate, adequate, and economic control, that it is flexible to a degree, and that it points to where corrective action should be applied.

CONTROLS MUST BE UNDERSTANDABLE   The first requirement of a workable control system is that the controls must be understandable. The supervisor who is to use controls must understand how they work and must understand what kind of controls he is to exercise over his employees. This is necessary on all managerial levels. There is no use designing a control system which the subordinates do not understand. The further down the system is to be applied the less complicated it must be. Therefore, a control system applied by the top administrator may be a very complicated system of controls based on mathematical formulae and statistical break-even charts, whereas the control system for the lower supervisory level will have to be much less complicated. It must be designed so that whoever is to use it will be able to understand it. If the control system given to the supervisor is of a complicated nature, it frequently happens that the first line supervisor will devise his own effective control system which, for all practical purposes, will fulfill the need. The same applies in the relationship between the supervisor and his employees. Whatever control system is devised, it must be designed in such fashion that it is understood.

CONTROLS MUST REGISTER DEVIATIONS QUICKLY   In order to have a workable control system, controls must indicate deviations without delay. As pointed out above, controls are forward-looking and the supervisor cannot control the past. However, in order that the controlling function will be most effective, it is important that the system is so designed that it will report deviations with speed. The sooner the supervisor is aware of deviations, the sooner he can take corrective action. Therefore, for control purposes it is more desirable to have deviations reported quickly, even if they are substantiated only by approximate figures and estimates, than to wait for the exact figures later on. It is far better for the supervisor to have approximate information that is prompt instead of having highly accurate information after it is too late to be of much value. This does not mean that the supervisor should jump to conclusions and take corrective action hastily. The supervisor's familiarity with the job to be done, his knowledge, and past experience, will come in handy in sensing quickly when a job is not progressing the way it should be. For most supervisors it is not necessary to wait until the day is over or the week is past to know whether the job will be or has been accomplished in time. His proximity to the employees makes it possible to observe deviations with speed.

CONTROLS MUST BE APPROPRIATE, ADEQUATE, AND ECONOMIC   Controls must be worth the expenses involved. It is obvious that an elaborate control system which is necessary in a large undertaking would not be needed in a small department. Nevertheless, the need for control exists just the same, only the magnitude of the control system will be different. Whatever controls the supervisor applies, it is essential that they must be appropriate for the job involved. There is no need to control a minor assignment as elaborately as the supervisor would control a major undertaking.

CONTROLS MUST BE FLEXIBLE AND POINT TO CORRECTIVE ACTION   Since all undertakings work in a dynamic situation, unforeseen circumstances and happenings could play havoc even with the best laid plans and standards. The control system must be built so that it will remain workable. It must be adequate to cope with the continuously changing pattern of a dynamic setting. It must permit change as soon as the change is required or else the control system is bound to fail. If the employee seems to run into changes of conditions early in his assignment, it is necessary for the supervisor to recognize this and to adjust the plans and standards accordingly. In other words, if early at the start all indications are that the assignment is running into unexpected difficulties due to conditions beyond the employee's reach, the supervisor must adjust the criteria by which he will check the employee's job.

It is not enough for a good control system to show deviations as they have occurred. The system must also indicate who is responsible for them and where they have occurred. The supervisor must make it his business to know precisely where the standards were not met and who is responsible for not coming up with standard output. If successive operations are involved, then it may be necessary for the supervisor to check the performance after each and every step has been accomplished and before the work has passed on to the next employee. Otherwise, if the end results are not as per standard the supervisor would not know where to take corrective action.

BASIC STEPS IN THE CONTROL PROCESS

In performing his controlling function the supervisor should follow the three basic steps outlined below: In order to be able to make certain whether or not the performance is in accordance with plans, it is necessary for the supervisor first to set standards. After setting these standards the supervisor should check the performance and appraise it. In so doing he will learn whether the performance has come up to the expected standards or not. In the latter case the supervisor takes corrective action, which is the third step. (see Figure 4) In order to control effectively it is necessary for the supervisor to follow these three basic steps in the sequence mentioned. As a matter of fact, he cannot check and report on deviations without having set the standards in advance, and he cannot take corrective action unless he has discovered that there are deviations from these standards.

THE SETTING OF STANDARDS   In order to control the work of any employee, it is necessary to check it against standards which are the criteria against which to judge results. The overall objectives of a hospital or related health facility are broken down into various objectives for the individual departments and within these departments the supervisor establishes objectives as to quality, production costs, production time, time standards, quotas, schedules, budgets, and many other specific standards for detailed operations. These goals become the criteria, the standards against

FIGURE 4

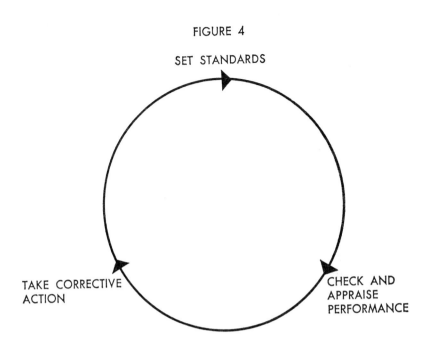

SET STANDARDS

TAKE CORRECTIVE
ACTION

CHECK AND
APPRAISE
PERFORMANCE

which the performance is measured. There are a multitude of standards by which the performance within a department can be appraised. Most of these, of course, are of a tangible nature, although there will be others which are intangible.

In setting these standards the supervisor is largely aided by his experience and by his knowledge of the various jobs to be done within his department. A supervisor has a general idea as to how much time it takes to perform a certain job, how much material it requires, what constitutes a good quality of performance, and what is a poor job. His job knowledge and experience within the activities which he supervises are one of the sources for establishing the standards against which he judges the performance within the department.

However, there are other more scientific and systematic ways of establishing objective standards. In many departments the supervisor can call on the help of industrial engineers who will help him in establishing standards for the amount of work an employee should turn out within a given period. In those departments where the nature of the work permits setting standards with the help of work measurement techniques, such procedure may be well worth the effort and cost. Standards arrived at in this way help the supervisor distribute the work evenly and judge fairly whether an employee is performing satisfactorily. Standards of this type make it possible for the supervisor to predict the number of employees required and the probable cost of a job to be done; in many industries, standards of this type serve as a basis for piece work and incentive plans.

The supervisor rarely conducts these work measurement techniques. They are usually assigned to an industrial engineer or an outside consultant. Setting standards in this fashion involves motion and time studies. Motion study involves an analysis of how the job is currently performed with a view to eliminating or combining certain steps, and devising a method which will be quicker and easier. In addition to this, flow charts are drawn up which analyze the steps taken in performing the jobs. After a thorough analysis of the motions and the work arrangements, the engineer will come up with what is considered the "best method" for doing the job in question. Once the "best method" has been designed, time studies are performed in order to find out the standard time required to do the job. All of this is done in a rather scientific and systematic method by selecting an employee for the observation, by observing the times used for the various elements of the job, by applying correction factors, and by making allowances for fatigue, personal time, unavoidable delays, and so on. All of this combined then leads to a standard time necessary to perform the job. Although this method sounds rather scientific it must be kept in mind that considerable judgment and many approximations will be at the basis of the standard time arrived. Results reached by motion and time studies are neither scientific nor beyond dispute. There is still the need for decisions involving judgment and discretion. However, they are a sound basis on which the supervisor will be able to determine objective standards.

If the supervisor should not have the assistance of industrial engineers available, he can perform some of this work himself by simply observing and timing the various operations and by making the necessary adjustments for fatigue, delay, and so on. If the job to be performed in the department has never been done there before, the supervisor should try to base his tentative standards on similar operations. If the new job has no similarity to any previous function then the best the supervisor can do—unless he can call on the help of industrial engineers—is to observe the operation while it is performed for the first few times. He will have to make these time and motion studies himself as best he can in order to arrive at a standard for this new function.

When setting standards the supervisor should bear in mind that the main purpose for doing so is to create effective standards. This means standards which can be achieved and are considered fair by both the supervisor and the employees. The standards are more likely to be effective if they are set with the participation of the supervisor and the subordinate instead of being handed down by a staff engineer and a top manager. The purpose of standards is to have a measure with which the performance of the worker can be compared and to give the supervisor a just cue for determining whether or not the employee has fallen down on the job, why, and what can be done about it.

In addition to the standards which can be expressed in physical terms and are tangible, there are also standards of an intangible nature. In a hospital or related health facility some of the intangible standards are good reputation in the city, high morale among the employees, and effective care of the patient so that his recovery is quick and his stay pleasant. It is exceedingly difficult, if not impossible, to express the criteria for such intangible standards in numerical and precise terms. Nevertheless, a supervisor should not overlook the intangible achievements even if it is difficult to set standards for them and just as difficult to measure their performance. Yet he must not overlook the importance of these intangible standards in achieving balanced performance in his department.

Strategic standards Obviously, the number of standards which can be used to ascertain the quality of performance within the department is very large and increases rapidly as a department expands. It becomes almost impossible for a supervisor to attempt to check the performance against all of the possible standards if his department is of any size. As the operations within the department become more complex and as the functions of the departments increase, it will become increasingly difficult for

is demoralizing to send reports to a supervisor who does not even read them.

Direct observation There is no substitute for direct observation and personal contact in the supervisor's function of checking on performance. There is no better way to check performance than by personally observing what is accomplished. Unfortunately, checking the performance through personal observation is time-consuming, but one of the regular duties of every supervisor is to spend a certain amount of his daily work in observing the performance of his employees. It is his job to personally inspect the operations and the results. It is, therefore, necessary for most supervisors to spend much of their time away from their office and away from their desks. This is the most effective way a supervisor can appraise the performance of his workers and keep his department functioning smoothly. In addition to this, his continued close personal contact with his employees is a part of the continuous training and development of his workers for more efficiency in their jobs. This opportunity for close personal observation is one of the advantages of the supervisor's job due to his closeness to the performance; this is something which the administrator cannot do to any great extent. The further removed a manager is from the firing line the less will he be able to personally observe, and the more will he have to depend on reports, whether they are with or without oral presentation.

Whenever the supervisor observes his employees at work he must assume a questioning attitude and not necessarily a fault-finding one. The supervisor should not ignore mistakes, but the manner in which he questions is very essential. He should ask himself whether or not there is any way in which he could help his employees do the job more easily, more safely, or more efficiently; whether there is anything about the way the employee is going about his job that should be particularly noticed, whether it is good or bad. Standards are stated in general terms but observations refer to definite instances such as specific actions, sloppy work, improperly performed jobs, etc. It may at times be difficult to convince an employee that "his work is unsatisfactory"; but if reference can be made to concrete cases it is easy to get the subordinate to recognize that they exist. It is essential for the supervisor to observe specifically because without being specific he cannot realistically appraise the performance and take whatever appropriate corrective action may be necessary.

CORRECTIVE ACTION   The third stage in the process of control is taking corrective action. The supervisor does not really control unless he takes corrective action if there is any need for it. Of course, if there are no deviations of performance from the established standards, then the supervisor's process of controlling is fulfilled by the first two steps. But if there is a discrepancy or a variation, then his controlling function is not fulfilled until and unless he has taken the third step, namely the step of corrective action. Data must be examined as quickly as possible after the observations are made, so that immediate corrective action can be taken in order to curb undesirable results and to bring performance back into line.

In case of deviations it is necessary for the supervisor first to make a careful check and analysis of the facts and to look for the reasons for the deviation. He must do this before he can prescribe any specific corrective action. The supervisor must bear in mind that the standards were based on certain prerequisites, forecasts, and assumptions, and these did not materialize. A check on the discrepancy may point out that the deviation was not caused by the employee in whose work it showed up, but in some work which preceded him. In such a case, of course, the corrective action must be directed toward the real source of the discrepancy. Another reason for the deviation may be that the employee is not qualified or that he has not been given the proper directions and instructions. If the employee is not qualified, additional training and supervision might help and then again, there might be cases where even additional training would not be sufficient. In this instance a replacement would be in order. There might be also a situation where directions have not been given properly and the employee was not well enough informed of what was expected of him. In this instance it is the supervisor's duty to again explain to his subordinate the standards which he is expected to maintain. It might also be helpful if the subordinate's motivation could be made stronger. The above are merely some of the reasons which may account for deviations from standards.

Only after a thorough analysis of the reasons for a deviation has been made will the supervisor be in a position to take corrective action. He must decide what remedial action may be necessary and what modifications for the future are necessary in order to secure improved results. This corrective action may consist of a revision of the standards, it may consist of replacing certain employees, or other means of getting things back in line. The supervisor, of course, must study the effect each corrective action may have on his control from now on. But unless and until he has taken corrective action he has not fulfilled his controlling function.

BUDGETS[1]

Of all available control devices, the budget is probably the one with which the supervisor has been in continuous contact and with which he has been coping for a long time. As a supervisor it is essential for him to learn to live with the budget which is assigned to him, and as a manager of his department it may be necessary for him to work out budgets for his department in cooperation with some first-line foremen who, in turn, may be supervising certain subgroups within the department. Therefore, it is essential for a supervisor to be familiar with the overall aspects of a budget.

As pointed out before, the making of a budget is planning but the administration of the budget is part of the controlling function. Budgets are pre-established standards to which operations are compared and adjusted by the exercise of control. A budget is a means of control insofar as it reflects the progress of the actual performance against the plan and in so doing it provides information which enables the supervisor to take action, if necessary, to make results conform with the plan.

The term budgeting usually refers to the preparations for the making of a plan which covers the operations for a definite period in the future. The budget states the anticipated results in specific numerical terms. Although the terms are usually of a monetary nature, not all budgets are expressed in dollars and

---

[1]See also the discussion on budgets in Chapter 7 "The Managerial Planning Function".

cents. There are many budgets which are stated in non-financial terms such as raw materials, which can be expressed in pounds, gallons, or yards. Then there are also personnel budgets which indicate the number of workers needed for each type of skill required, and state the man hours allocated for certain activities.

The making of a budget, whether it is financial or otherwise, leads to improved planning. For budgetary purposes it is not sufficient just to make a general statement. It is necessary to quantify and state specific plans. There is a considerable difference between making a general forecast on one hand and attaching numerical values to specific plans on the other. The figures which are put into the budget are the actual plan which will become the standard of achievement. Every manager is concerned with the budget and it is not only necessary that top administration give it its complete support, but it is just as essential that those supervisors who will administer and function under these budgets have a part in preparing them.

It seems to be natural for people to resent arbitrary orders, and it is imperative that all budget allowances and objectives are determined with the full cooperation of those who are responsible for executing the plan. Therefore, the supervisor should have an opportunity to participate in the making of the budget with which he is to work for the coming period. The budget is usually made out, at least on the supervisory level, for one year and not longer. Aside from the one-year budgets it is quite common for top administration to have other budgets which extend for some years in advance.

The supervisor should keep in mind the fact that budgets are merely a tool for management and not a substitute for good judgment. Also, care should be taken not to make budgets so detailed that they become cumbersome. Budgets should always allow the supervisor enough freedom to accomplish the best objectives of his department. There must be a reasonable degree of latitude and flexibility. Realizing that a budget should never become a straitjacket, enlightened management assures flexibility of the budget by means of regular budget revisions. At regular intervals the established budget is reviewed by the supervisor and his boss, and at that time actual preformance will be checked and compared with the budget. If operating conditions have appreciably changed and if there are valid indications that the budget cannot be followed in the future, a revision of the budgetary program is in order. Such circumstances may be caused by unexpected events, unexpected wage increases, or fluctuation in the general economic climate. Such regular review and revision ought to take place, if not every three months, at least every six months. Only with the help of a regular budget review and revision can a necessary degree of flexibility for a budgetary program be assured.

Budgets necessarily represent restrictions, and for this reason subordinates generally do not like budgets. It often happens that subordinates have a defensive approach to budgets, an approach which they often acquire through painful experience. Many times the subordinates become acquainted with budgets only as a barrier to spending; or the budget is blamed for failure to get a raise in salary. The term "budget" in the minds of many subordinates often has become associated with miserly behavior rather than with planning and direction. It is the supervisor's job to point out that budgeting is a trained and disciplined approach to all problems. The subordinate should be assured that there is enough flexibility built into the budget system to permit good common sense departures which will serve the best interests of the enterprise. This ultimately will lead the subordinate to feel that whatever can be done without a budget can be done better with one.

OTHER CONTROL DEVICES   Aside from the budget, the supervisor has other control devices at his disposal. Mention should be made of more scientific tools and statistical data which the supervisor has available. Statistical data can be presented either in form of tables and charts or in the form of curves. There are other kinds of pictorial presentations which can be used for controlling purposes. But a discussion of these would be beyond the scope of this text. If the supervisor wishes to explore some of these more scientific approaches and use them within his controlling function he would do well to call on someone within the organization who is familiar with mathematics and other statistical procedures.

SUMMARY   Control is a managerial function which determines whether or not plans are adhered to and whether preformance is up to standards. It is one of the five managerial functions without which the managerial process is not complete. Controlling influences the other managerial functions, and it in turn is influenced by the others. Controls are forward-looking, as there is nothing which can be done about the past. To be effective the control system must be understandable, it must register deviations quickly, it must be appropriate, and economic. It must be flexible and it must point out where corrective action should be taken. In performing the controlling function, the manager should follow certain basic steps. He first must set standards, then he must check performance, and third, he must take corrective action. In the setting of standards the supervisor must be aware of intangible and tangible standards. The latter group can be established with the help of motion and time studies. It is much more difficult, if not almost impossible, to establish standards for intangible aspects. Since the number of standards is so large the supervisor will do well to select certain control points as strategic ones. In each and every department the supervisor alone can best determine which these are. After establishing the standards, it is the supervisor's function to check and appraise performance against them. In some instances he will have to depend on reports, but in most instances direct personal observation and inspection is the best means for appraising performance. If discrepancies from standards are revealed the supervisor must take corrective action in order to bring matters back into line. In addition to various pictorial control devices such as charts, graphs, and statistical approaches, the budget is the most widely used control device. Budget making is planning, whereas budget administration is controlling. In order for a supervisor to be able to work well with the budget it is necessary that he has participated in its preparation, that he fully understands it and its limitations. By the same token, it is necessary for the boss to understand the limitations of the budget and the various human problems involved. Good budget administration is achieved only when every supervisor feels that whatever can be done without a budget can be done so much better with one.

PART VII

LABOR RELATIONS

18

THE SUPERVISOR AND THE UNION

There is little doubt that the introduction of a union into
the management of a hospital or related health facility may be
a traumatic experience for a supervisor as well as for the administrator. It may bring a time of tension during which constructive solutions of problems may be difficult. Gradually, however, both sides, namely the union and the administration, learn
to live with each other. Every manager must accept the fact
that the trade union is a permanent force in our society. Every
manager must realize that the union, just as any other institution, has in it the potential either for advancing or for disrupting
the common effort of the institution. It is in the self-interest of the
administration to create a labor-management climate which directs these potentialities toward constructive ends. There is no
simple or magic formula for overnight cultivation of a favorable climate which will result in cooperation and mutual understanding. It takes wisdom and sensitivity for every manager of
the organization, from the administrator down to the supervisor,
to show in the day-to-day relationship that the union is accepted
as a responsible organization.

In this effort to create and maintain a constructive pattern
of cooperation between the hospital and the union the most

significant single factor is the supervisor of a department. It is the supervisor who in his day-to-day relations with the employees makes the labor agreement a living document for better or for worse. Therefore, the continuous training in and awareness of supervisors of the fundamentals of collective bargaining and of the nature of labor agreements is essential in the development of good labor relations. The supervisor is involved in union relations primarily in two distinct phases: first, in the phase of negotiations, and second, in the day-to-day administration of the agreement, which includes the handling of complaints and grievances. Although the supervisor is primarily concerned with the latter aspects of relations with the union, he also plays a role in the first one.

THE SUPERVISOR AND LABOR NEGOTIATIONS

On the surface it does not look as if the supervisor is significantly involved in the negotiations of a labor agreement. The period when a union is first entering a department of a hospital or related health facility is usually filled with tensions. Emotions run high and considerable disturbance takes place. Under such conditions it is understandable that the delicate negotiations of a union contract are carried on only by the members of top administration. There usually is an air of secrecy surrounding the negotiations, which are often carried on in a hotel or at a lawyer's office. Since a committee of the employees is participating in these negotiations there exists a fast line of communication with the employees of the hospital but not necessarily with the supervisor. The latter often runs the danger of being less well informed about the course of negotiations than his subordinates are. Therefore, the administrator must make it his business to keep the supervisor fully informed as to the course which the negotiations are taking. In addition to this, he should give the supervisor an opportunity to express his opinions in reference to the matters which are brought up during the negotiations, because in the final analysis the supervisor bears the major responsibility for fulfilling the contract provisions. This exchange of information is essential when negotiations first begin.

The same necessity exists whenever the annual or bi-annual re-negotiations of the labor agreement arise. At that time it is also necessary to consult with the supervisor as to how specific provisions in the contract have worked out and what changes in the contract the supervisor would like to have made. It is essential for the administrator and the supervisor to realize that although the supervisor does not sit at the labor negotiations table, he has a great deal to do with negotiating. Many of the demands the union brings up during the negotiations have their origin in the day-to-day operations of the department. Many of the difficult questions which must be solved in the bargaining process stem from the relationship which the supervisor has with his employees in his department. Therefore, it is obvious that there will be a great amount of checking back and forth between the administrator and the supervisor during the time of negotiating a labor agreement. In order to supply valuable information the supervisor must not only know what has been going on in his department, but he must be aware of the facts in order to substantiate his statements. This points to the value of keeping good records of incidents, production, leaves, promotions, and similar happenings. The supervisor should be alert to problem situations which he can call to the administrator's attention so that in the next negotiations these matters may be worked out in order for the problem not to arise again. It is in the interest of the union and the institution to have as small a number of unresolved problems as possible. While it is the responsibility of the administrator to negotiate the initial labor agreement and to negotiate a new one whenever it must be renewed, the supervisor is also deeply involved in this, although he does not sit at the negotiating table.

THE SUPERVISOR AND THE CONTENT OF THE AGREEMENT
Once the administration and the union have agreed upon a labor contract, this agreement will be the document according to which both parties have to operate. Since the supervisor now has the obligation to manage his department within the overall framework of this labor agreement it is of prime necessity that he have complete knowledge of the provisions of the union contract and how these provisions are to be interpreted. The supervisor, in his daily relations with his employees, has the responsibility for carrying out the clauses of the contract; therefore, he must be thoroughly familiar with all parts of the contract. Since

the first line supervisor is the one who can cause disagreements between the union and the hospital by failing to live up to the terms of the agreement, the content of the contract must be fully known to and understood by him.

It is therefore necessary for the administrator to arrange for meetings between all the supervisors and himself and to brief the supervisors on the content of the labor contract, giving them an opportunity to ask questions about any part which they do not understand. Copies of the contract and clarification of the various clauses must be furnished to the supervisors so that they know what they can and what they cannot do. Since there are no two contracts alike, it is impossible to pinpoint certain provisions which the supervisor should check into. Normally, all contracts deal with matters of pay, such as hourly rates, bonus rates, conditions and hours of work, overtime, vacations, leaves of absences, promotions, and similar matters. Almost certainly there are provisions covering the complaint and grievance procedures. But in addition to this there are many other provisions which are peculiar to each institution in question.

It is not only necessary for the administrator to familiarize the supervisors with the exact provisions of the contract, it is just as important to explain to them the thinking of the administrator in reference to relations with the union, the administrator's philosophy and general attitude toward the agreement. The supervisors should understand that it is the intention of the administration to achieve harmonious working conditions with the union so that the hospital objectives are achieved in the most ideal fashion. The administrator should clarify the fact that the only way to create harmonious relations in a hospital or related health facility is by effective contract administration. The administrator must clarify to the supervisors that coherent relations between the hospital, its employees, and the union depend upon the way in which the supervisor handles the contract on a day-to-day basis. There will still be enough areas of conflict. But without this kind of general attitude and understanding the number of conflicts would be greater.

It is important for the supervisor to bear in mind that the negotiated contract was carefully and thoughtfully worked out, and finally agreed upon by both parties. It is not in the interest of successful contract administration for the supervisor to try to "beat the contract," even though he may think he is doing the institution a favor. The administrator must make it clear that in order to achieve harmonious cooperation the supervisor may not construct his own contractual clauses as he would like to have them or interpret them in his own way. Once the agreement has been reached the supervisor should not attempt to beat the contract or to circumvent it.

If the administrator should fail to familiarize his supervisor with the provisions and the spirit of the agreement, the supervisor should insist on such briefing sessions and explanations before he applies the clauses of the contract in the daily working situation of his department. The advent of the labor agreement does not change the supervisor's job as a manager. He still must get his job done by planning, organizing, staffing, directing, and controlling. There is no change in the authority delegated to him by the administrator or the responsibility which he has accepted. The significant change which takes place is that he must now perform his managerial duties within the framework of the terms of the union agreement. He still has the right to require his subordinates to carry out his orders; he still has the obligation to get the job done within his department. But there are likely to be certain provisions within the union agreement which delineate and even influence his activities. In our discussion of authority it was stated that there are limitations to the concept of authority and in all likelihood the union agreement spells out some of these, especially within the areas of disciplinary action and dismissal. Undoubtedly, in many instances the provisions of the contract make it difficult for the supervisor to be a good manager. But the only way to overcome this is to improve his own managerial facilities as well as the knowledge and techniques of good labor relations.

THE SUPERVISOR AND CONTRACT ADMINISTRATION

It is in the day-to-day administration of the labor agreement that the real importance of the supervisor's contribution shows up. The manner in which he handles the day-to-day problems within the framework of the labor agreement will either make for good or poor union-management relationships. The contract is an agreement in name only, until and unless the supervisor knows how to make it work from day to day. The best contract written will do little good if it is poorly administered by the man on the firing line. The administrator may have done all within his power to draw up the best possible contract and to indoctrinate the supervisors with the content of the various clauses. It is the daily application and administration of the agreement which will make the difference between harmonious labor-management relations and a situation filled with unnecessary tensions and bad feelings. At best, a labor contract sets forth only the broad outline of the labor-management relationships. To make it a positive instrument of constructive management-labor relations the agreement must be filled in with appropriate and intelligent supervisory decisions. It is the supervisor who interprets the administrator's intent by his everyday actions. In the final analysis it is the supervisor who, with his decisions and actions and attitude, really gives the contract meaning and life.

In many instances it is true that the supervisor for all practical purposes often "rewrites" many of the provisions of the labor agreement when he interprets and applies them to specific situations. In so doing the supervisor sets precedents to which arbitrators pay heed when deciding grievances which come before them. It is impossible for the administrator and the union to draw up a contract which anticipates every possible situation that could occur in employee relations and to specify directives for their solutions. Therefore, the individual judgment of the supervisor becomes very important in deciding a particular situation. This illustrates the vast significance of the supervisor's influence on the content of the labor agreement. Since the supervisor represents administration, any error in his decisions is the administration's error. It is the immediate supervisor on whom the greatest responsibility falls to see that the clauses of the agreement are carried out appropriately. It is, therefore, necessary for the administrator to realize how significant a role the supervisor plays in the contract administration, and it is just as essential for the supervisor to realize how far-reaching his decisions are.

There are usually two broad areas in which the supervisor is likely to run into difficulties in the administration of the labor agreement. The first broad area of difficulty covers the vast number of complaints which are concerned with single issues. These are: grievances in the case of disciplinary action, assignment of work, distribution of overtime, transfer, the question of promotion or downgrading, and other grievances of this sort. In each of these situations the personal judgment of the supervisor is of great importance and he should feel free to dispose of these grievances if he thinks that he is clear on the contract provisions and complying with them. In situations of this type his actions must be consistent. Since no two people ever look on a problem in the same manner, a good amount of personal judgment will be involved in the decisions of this type; but the supervisor must see to it that his decisions are consistent.

The second broad area covers those grievances and problems in which the supervisor is called upon to interpret a clause of the contract. The supervisor finds himself in a situation where he attempts to carry out the generalized statement of the contract and the problem is one of interpretation. In this instance it would be wrong for the supervisor to handle the problem without consulting with higher management. Whenever the interpretation of the contract is the issue, any decision is likely to be long-lasting. It therefore would be unwise for a supervisor to interpret a certain provision of the agreement in a particular sense without first consulting his superior; such a decision may set a precedent which the hospital may never be able to set aside later on. It may very well be that the union would base its attitude on this precedent, and it is very likely that even an arbitrator would make a decision based on such a previous decision. Therefore, whenever interpretation of a clause is in doubt the question should be brought to the attention of the supervisor's boss. Although the supervisor has been well indoctrinated with the clauses, the meaning, and the philosophy of the contract, it is likely that in a dynamic setting in which the labor agreement operates problems will come up which will necessitate interpretation of the meaning by the administrator.

THE SUPERVISOR'S RIGHT TO DECIDE　　In the daily administration of the labor agreement the supervisor must bear in mind the fact that as a member of management he has the right and even the duty to make a decision. The supervisor must realize that the union contract does not abrogate management's right to make the decisions; it is still management's prerogative to do so. However, the union has a right to protest the decision. For instance, it is the supervisor's job to maintain discipline and if he should see that disciplinary action is necessary, he should take it without first discussing the issue with the union's representative. The supervisor should understand that there is no joint co-determination clause and he should not set any precedent of determining together with the union what the supervisor's rights in a particular disciplinary case are. Of course, before he takes disciplinary action every wise supervisor will see to it that he has examined all aspects of a situation, has taken all preliminary steps, and thought through the appropriateness of his action. Since repercussions from the union are likely to occur, the supervisor must have a good case before he takes action. But the right to decide is with him and him alone.

THE SUPERVISOR'S DUTY TO ACT   Coupled with the supervisor's right to make decisions is his duty to take action against employees who do not comply with the contract provisions. It is the supervisor's job to see to it that the contract is kept alive and that all provisions are observed and enforced. Any neglect on his part to take action may be interpreted to mean that the institution has decided to drop these provisions from the contract. Any inaction on the supervisor's part in this respect could set a precedent and could be interpreted to mean that the provisions have been set aside. It is the supervisor's duty to make certain that the contract is kept alive, and he must take appropriate action whenever the occasion calls for it.

THE SUPERVISOR AND THE SHOP STEWARD   The supervisor will probably have most contact with the shop steward who is the lowest official of the union and who is sometimes referred to as shop committeeman. The shop steward is an employee of a hospital or related health facility who is expected to put in a full day's work for his employer and who has been elected by his fellow workers to be their official spokesman both with the institution and with the union local. This, obviously, is a difficult position since the steward has to serve two masters. As an employee he is expected to put in a full day's work for the employer, has to follow his orders and directives; as a union official he has responsibilities to the group of employees who elected him and to the local union.

Just as individuals vary in their approach to their jobs, so do stewards vary in their approach to their position. Some are unassuming; others are overbearing. Some are helpful and courteous and others are difficult. Unless there are special provisions, the steward's rights are merely those of any other union member. He is subject to the same regulations as to workmanship and conduct as every other employee of the department. Certain privileges usually are specified in the union contract which states how much company time can be devoted to union business or other matters, whether or not solicitation of membership, collection of dues, etc., may be carried on during working hours, and a number of other provisions.

As stated above, the role of the steward will depend considerably upon the makeup of the individual. There are those who will take advantage of their position to do as little work as possible; others will perform a good day's work. The supervisor should always remember that the steward is an employee of the hospital and should be treated as such. But he should also remember that the steward is the elected representative of the employees and as such the steward learns quickly what the employees are thinking and what is going on in the "grapevine." The union will see to it that he is well informed as to the content of the labor agreement and as to management's prerogatives and the employees' rights. The supervisor must understand the dual role of the union steward and a proper understanding can make him a good link between the supervisor and the employees.

The most important responsibility of a shop steward probably is in relation to complaints and grievances coming from the employees. It is the supervisor's job to settle complaints and to adjust grievances. In this role the supervisor represents management whereas the steward represents the employee for the union. In most cases the steward is sincere in trying to represent the employees who have a grievance and once a grievance has been submitted a good steward will always try to win it. In all union contracts the procedures for handling complaints and grievances are described in great detail and the steward, together with the supervisor, will follow the prescribed steps. The settlement of grievances will be discussed in more detail, but for the present it is sufficient to note only that one of the steward's chief responsibilities is to present complaints and grievances along with the aggrieved employee to the supervisor and the management.

In order for the shop steward to be an effective grievance handler he must understand the work of the employees, he must understand job assignment, and he must understand the working of the labor agreement. Once elected he should convince the employees that they can rely on him, and through him on the union, to protect them. At times the supervisor may be under the impression that the shop steward is out looking for grievances in order to stay busy. This may truly be so since he has a political assignment and since it is necessary to assure the workers that the union is working in their behalf. On the other hand, an experienced steward knows that there normally are a sufficient amount of real grievances to be settled and that there is no need to look for complaints which do not have a valid background and which would rightfully be turned down by the supervisor.

The union will see to it that the shop steward is well trained to present complaints and grievances so that they can be carried to a successful conclusion. Once a grievance has been submitted, a good steward will always try to win it. Before presenting a grievance a shop steward will determine such matters as whether or not the contract has been violated, whether the company acted unfairly, whether the employee's health or safety has been put in jeopardy, etc., etc. In grievance matters the union is on the offensive and the supervisor is on the defensive. The shop steward will challenge the management decision or action and the supervisor must justify what he has done.

Obviously, the shop steward's interest is in his membership, and in so doing he may at times antagonize the supervisor. Under those conditions it is difficult for the supervisor to keep a sense of humor and to keep his temper. It is often difficult for a supervisor to discuss a grievance with a shop steward on an equal footing since he is, within the normal working situation, a subordinate in his department. But whenever he wears the hat of the shop steward his position as the elected representative of the union members gives him equal standing. The supervisor should always bear in mind that the steward's job is a political job and as such carries with it certain implications. On the other hand, he should also understand that a good shop steward will keep the supervisor on his toes and force him to be a better manager.

SUMMARY   The supervisor's role in the relations of a hospital or related health facility with a union cannot be minimized. Although the supervisor normally is not a member of the management team when it sits down with the union negotiators to settle the terms of the labor contract, he plays an important role in this meeting. Many of the difficulties and problems discussed at these meetings can be traced directly back to the daily activities of the supervisor. At best, a labor contract sets forth only the broad outline of the labor-management relationships. It is the day-to-day application and administration of the agreement which will make the difference between harmonious labor relations and a situation filled with unnecessary tensions and bad feelings. The supervisor is the person who, through his daily decisions and actions, gives the contract real meaning. He therefore must be thoroughly familiar with the contents of the contract and the general philosophy of the administration of the hospital in relation to the union. He must understand the important role of the union steward, who in his dual capacity is one of the employees and at the same time the elected representative of the union members. He is the one who is on the offensive and out to win his case. The supervisor is on the defensive.

19

ADJUSTING GRIEVANCES

All the foregoing discussion points to the necessity for the supervisor to be well qualified in handling complaints and settling grievances. Since one of his main duties is to make certain that all complaints and grievances are properly disposed of at the first step, the supervisor must be capable of coping with the problems and of settling them.

The supervisor must know that the handling of grievances is part of the regular day's work and that it takes judgment, tact, and often more patience than comes naturally. He may often feel that much of his time is taken up in discussing complaints and grievances instead of getting the job done in his department. Often he may feel that he has to be more of a labor lawyer than a supervisor. The supervisor's skill in handling the grievances is an index of his ability as a supervisor of his department. The number of grievances that come up within his group is often a good indication of the state of the employee-management relations.

Although a fine distinction can be made between the terms dissatisfaction, complaints, and grievances, in everyday language a grievance simply means a complaint which has been formally presented either to the supervisor as a management representative, or to the shop steward or any other union official. Normally, it is a complaint resulting from a misunderstanding, interpretation, or violation of the provisions of the labor agreement. The supervisor must learn to distinguish between those grievances that are admissible and those gripes which indicate the employee is unhappy or dissatisfied. In the latter case the supervisor should by all means listen to what the employee has to say in order to learn what is bothering him and in order to decide whether or not this is a grievance resulting from a misunderstanding, interpretation, or a violation of the contract.

THE STEWARD'S ROLE IN GRIEVANCE PROCEDURE   The steward is usually the spokesman for the employee in the grievance procedure. He is familiar with the labor agreement and has been well indoctrinated as to how to present the employee's side of the grievance. A good shop steward is eager to get the credit for settling a grievance. Therefore, the question arises as to what the supervisor should do when the employee approaches him without the shop steward, or without having consulted the shop steward. In such a case it is appropriate for the supervisor to listen to the employee's story and to see whether or not the case he submits is of interest to the union and if the union is involved at all. If the indications are that the contract or the union are involved, then the supervisor should by all means call in the shop steward to listen to the employee's presentation. Although it is unlikely that a union member would present a grievance without the shop steward, the supervisor will do well to observe the above suggestion.

On the other hand, if the steward submits a grievance himself, the supervisor should listen to him sympathetically and carefully. It is always best to listen to complaints when both the steward and the complaining employee are present. But if the shop steward does not bring the employee along it still is necessary to listen to what the steward has to say. There is nothing to keep the supervisor from speaking with the employee directly either in conjunction with the steward or without the shop steward. In the latter situation the supervisor should take great care not to give the impression that he is undermining the steward's authority or the steward's relationship to the union membership. There should be free and easy communication between the supervisor and the shop steward. In most situations the shop steward will present the grievance accompanied by the aggrieved employee. It is the job of the shop steward to represent employees and to fight hard to win their case.

THE SUPERVISOR'S ROLE IN ADJUSTING GRIEVANCES   It is one of the supervisor's prime functions to dispose of all grievances at the first step of the grievance procedure. It is the supervisor's job to explore the details of the grievance fully and to cope with the problems brought out and to try to settle them.

The supervisor will quickly learn that it pays to settle grievances early, before they grow from molehills into mountains. There are some unusual grievance cases which may have to be referred to the higher levels of management. But normally grievances should be settled in the first step. If many grievances go beyond this step, it may indicate that the supervisor is not carrying out his duties properly. Unless circumstances are beyond the supervisor's control he should make all efforts to handle grievances brought to his attention within reasonable time limits and to bring them to a successful conclusion. In order to achieve satisfactory adjustments of grievances at this early stage the supervisor will do well to observe the following check list:

1. *Be available* The supervisor must see to it that he is easily available to the shop steward and to the aggrieved employee. Availability does not only mean being physically around. It means being approachable and ready to listen with an open mind. The supervisor must not make it difficult for a complaining employee to see him and to sound off.

2. *Learn how to listen* Everything which has been discussed in the chapters on communication and interviewing is applicable to this situation also. When the complaint is brought to the supervisor, the steward and the employee should be given the opportunity to present their case fully. Sympathetic listening is likely to minimize hostilities and tensions when the steward presents the case. The supervisor must know how to listen well. When the grievance is called to his attention he must give the steward and the employee a chance to say whatever they have on their chests. If they gain the impression that he is truly listening to them and that the supervisor will give them fair treatment the complaint will not loom as large to them as it did. It can happen that halfway through the story the complaining employee realizes that he does not have a real complaint at all. Sympathetic listening can often produce this result. It sometimes happens that the more a person talks the more likely he is to make contradictory and inconsistent remarks, thus weakening his own argument. Only good listening can produce this.

3. *Do not get angry* The supervisor must take great caution not to get angry at the shop steward. He must understand that

259

it is the steward's job to represent the employee even in those cases where he knows and feels that the grievance is not valid. In such a situation it is the supervisor's job to point out that there are no merits in this grievance. The supervisor cannot expect the shop steward to do this for him as he must serve as the employees' spokesman at all times. Sometimes, for particular reasons, a union deliberately creates grievances to keep things stirred up. Even such a situation must not arouse the anger of the supervisor. If he does not know how to handle such occurrences successfully then he will do well to discuss it with upper management and experts in the labor relations department. But by no means must he get upset even if the grievances are phony.

4. Define the problem In order to determine whether the grievance is a valid grievance under the contract, it is necessary to define the employee's complaint and the extent of the problem. Often the shop steward and the employee are not particularly clear in this respect and it is then the supervisor's job to summarize what has been presented, and to make certain that this is the problem about which the complaint is. Often the complaint merely deals with symptoms, whereas the problem lies much deeper. Unless the problem is clearly brought out and discussed, occurrences of a similar nature will happen again and again. But once the problem is clarified it is not likely that grievances of the same type will come up again. In summarizing the problem, the supervisor must use clear layman's language and not resort to legalistic terminology.

5. Get the facts In order to arrive at a solution of the problem and the adjustment of the grievance it becomes necessary to have the facts. The supervisor should ask the complaining employee pertinent questions which may bring out inconsistencies. In so doing the supervisor must be objective and try not to confuse either the shop steward or the employee. The supervisor must ascertain who, what, when, where, and why. The supervisor should obtain all those facts which he can obtain without any undue delay. Although he may sometimes be inclined to hide behind the excuse of searching for more facts he must not do so. He must decide on those facts which he has available and can quickly obtain. He must find out what caused the grievance, where it happened, whether there was unfair treatment, intentionally, deliberately, or not. He must determine whether there is any connection between this grievance and another grievance, and so on. Frequently it is impossible to gather all the information at once, and therefore it will not be feasible to settle the grievance right away. Under those conditions it is necessary to tell the complaining employee and the shop steward about this. If they see that the supervisor is working on the problem, they are likely to be reasonable and wait for an answer.

6. *Know your contract* After having determined the facts, it is now essential for the supervisor to ascertain whether or not this is a legitimate grievance in the meaning of the contract. Usually a grievance is not a grievance in the legal sense unless provisions of the labor contract have been violated or administered inconsistently. Therefore, it is necessary to check the provisions in the contract when any reference to a violation of it is made. If the supervisor has any question about this it would be wise for him to get advice from his own boss or from the labor relations department as to how to handle the problem in question. It may be that changes have been made in the contract, and the supervisor must acquaint himself with their intent and meaning, and how they are to be interpreted.

7. *Do not delay* The supervisor must see to it that all grievances are settled as promptly and justly as possible. Postponing an adjustment in the hope that the grievance may disappear is courting trouble and more grievances. Speed is essential in the settlement of grievances, but of course not if it will result in unsound decisions. The employee and the steward are entitled to know the supervisor's position as quickly as he can get the facts. If it is impossible for the supervisor to obtain the necessary facts at once, he must let the aggrieved parties know about this instead of leaving them under the impression that he is giving them the run-around. Waiting for a decision is bothersome to everybody concerned, and speed is therefore of utmost importance.

8. *Adjust grievances at an early stage* It is part of the supervisor's job to see that all grievances are properly adjusted at the first step of the grievance procedure. This is part of the managerial aspects of the supervisor's job. Only those cases

should be referred to the higher levels of management which are of an unusual nature or which require additional interpretation of the meaning of the union contract, or contain problems which have not shown up heretofore.

9. *Be consistent* In the adjustment of grievances the supervisor must make certain that he protects the rights of the administration and follows the policies of the hospital and precedents. If the circumstances are such that he must deviate from previous adjustments it is necessary for him to explain the reason for this to the employee and the shop steward; and he must make certain that both of them understand that this exception does not set a precedent. In such instances it is always wise to check with higher levels of the administration or with the labor relations department.

10. *Give a clear answer* The supervisor must answer in a straightforward, reasonable manner—a way which the aggrieved parties can understand and is clear to them. It must not be phrased in language which they cannot understand, regardless of whether or not the adjustment is in favor of an employee. If the supervisor disagrees with the employee he is that much more entitled to a clear and straightforward reply. He may disagree with it, but, at least he will understand it. This is so much more important if the supervisor has to reply to the grievance in writing. If a written reply is necessary he must restrict his answer to the specific complaints and must make certain that the words he uses are the appropriate ones and that any reference to a particular provision of the labor agreement or plant rules are the ones in question. Unless a supervisor is forced to, he should not render a written reply. However, if this is part of the labor agreement, then it is appropriate for him to discuss all the implications with higher management or the personnel department so that when he has to write his answer to the employee a standard set of replies are at his fingertips.

11. *Consider the consequences of the settlement* Since the supervisor's decision becomes precedent, he must consider what the effect of the adjustment of the grievance will mean in this particular instance and also for the future. He must bear in mind that each and every time he settles a grievance he sets a precedent and that much of it will show up as part of the labor contract in following years. It is therefore advisable to keep track of past settlements and to check with them to make certain that the decision is consistent with what he has done before, with the institution's policy, and the labor agreement.

12. *Keep records* It is essential for the supervisor to keep records whenever he makes a decision. If he satisfies the employee's request his decision will become a precedent. If he cannot settle the complaint there is a likelihood that this grievance will go to arbitration. It certainly will go to higher levels of management, and it is difficult, if not impossible, for the supervisor to defend his actions by depending on his memory. Therefore, it is necessary for the supervisor to keep diligent records of the facts, his reasoning and his decision. With this at hand he will be able to substantiate his decision when he is asked for explanations. Good records are an absolute necessity. Since the burden of proof is on the supervisor he must make certain that he can justify his decisions and actions. It is correct to state that management has the right to manage but that the union has the right to grieve. Whenever the employee or the union maintains that the supervisor has violated the agreement or administered its provisions in an unfair or inconsistent manner, the supervisor must justify his action, and without good records this will often be difficult, if not impossible.

The supervisor should familiarize himself with the foregoing twelve points as aids in handling grievances. In order to live up to his responsibilities as a manager it is part of his job to settle grievances and to make decisions at the early stage of the procedure. No doubt the supervisor's decisions and actions have a heavy impact on the employee-union relations of a hospital and related health facility. Not only must he be familiar with the above-mentioned points, he must also acquire an ability to carry on face-to-face discussions with the employee and the shop steward whenever these disputes arise.

SUMMARY The labor agreement sets forth only a general broad outline of labor-management relationships. This broad outline must be filled in with intelligent supervisory decisions; occasions to make such decisions arise mainly in the settlement of complaints and grievances. The proper adjustment of grievances is one of the important components of the supervisory position. Whenever the supervisor settles grievances he applies and interprets the labor agreement, and his decisions have far-reaching implications due to the fact that they set precedents. Much of what the union will discuss at the next contract negotiations has its origin in the day-to-day supervisory decisions. And if the grievance should go to arbitration, the impartial arbitrator attaches great importance to precedent. Often it is not so much what the contract says that counts, but how it has been interpreted by management's front line representative, namely the supervisor. This shows how important a role the supervisor plays in the adjustment of grievances and how necessary it is for him to gain more and more skill in it.

In order to adjust grievances appropriately the supervisor will do well to be always available and to listen, without losing his temper, even if the grievance is a "phony" one. He must learn to define the problem, get the facts, and then draw on his thorough knowledge of the contract. It is important to avoid unnecessary delays and to settle grievances at an early stage; the supervisor must be fair in his decisions, protecting the rights of the institution and respecting the content and spirit of the agreement; he must keep good records, give clear replies, and above all, remain consistent.

INDEX